APE
INTO
MAN

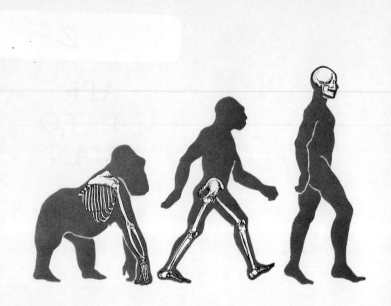

APE INTO MAN

A Study of Human Evolution

S. L. WASHBURN
University of California, Berkeley

RUTH MOORE

Little, Brown and Company

BOSTON

LIBRARY OF CONGRESS CATALOG CARD NO. 73-2811

THIRD PRINTING

*Published simultaneously in Canada
by Little, Brown & Company (Canada) Limited*

PRINTED IN THE UNITED STATES OF AMERICA

CREDITS FOR ILLUSTRATIONS

The sources for the illustrations appear below. The artwork has, for the most part, been redrawn. The artists are V. Susan Fox (Figures 1.1, 1.3, 2.3, 2.8, 2.10, 3.2, 3.3, 3.4, 3.6, 4.2, 5.3, 6.1, 6.2, 6.3, 6.9, and chapter opening illustration); Richard H. Sanderson (Figures 1.6, 4.3, 6.4, 6.5, 6.6, 6.7, and 6.8); and Eric Stoelting (Figures 2.1, 2.5, and 2.6). The authors wish to thank the publishers, authors, photographers, and illustrators for granting permission to use their material. The figures without specified credits have been drawn for this book.

Cover collage by Rob Polomski, based on the following figures: 2.8, 3.3, 3.4, 3.6, and 6.9. See figure sources below.

Chapter 1: Chapter opening drawn from a photograph by Ralph Morse in *The Primates*; © 1965 Time Inc. 1.2 From "Hominid Fossils from the Area East of Lake Rudolf, Kenya: Photographs and a Commentary on Context" by Richard E. Leakey and Glynn Ll. Isaac, in *Perspectives on Human Evolution 2*, edited by S. L. Washburn and Phyllis Dolhinow. Copyright © 1972 by Holt, Rinehart and Winston, Inc. Reproduced by permission of Holt, Rinehart and Winston, Inc. 1.3 Chimpanzee drawn from a photograph in Jane van Lawick-Goodall, *In the Shadow of Man* (Boston: Houghton Mifflin, 1971); copyright © 1971 by Hugo and Jane van Lawick-Goodall. 1.4 From David E. Kohne, "Excerpts from Evolution of Primate DNA," *Engineering and Science* 33 (April 1970): 25, by permission of the author. 1.5 Allan C. Wilson and Vincent M. Sarich.

Chapter 2: 2.2 Brian O'Connor. 2.3 Adapted with permission of Macmillan Publishing Co., Inc. from *Primate Evolution* by Elwyn L. Simons, Fig. 12, p. 155. Copyright © 1972 by Elwyn L. Simons. 2.7 From *Historia Naturalis* by Ulysses Aldrovandus, 1642. 2.8 Drawn from a photograph in Jane van Lawick-Goodall, *In the Shadow of Man* (Boston: Houghton Mifflin, 1971); copyright © 1971 by Hugo and Jane van Lawick-Goodall. 2.9 From *In the Shadow of Man.* Copyright © 1971 by Hugo and Jane van Lawick-Goodall. Reprinted by permission of Houghton Mifflin Company. 2.10 Drawn from a photograph in *Scientific American* 217 (December 1967): 29, by permission of Lee Boltin.

Chapter 3: 3.1 S. L. Washburn. 3.2 Drawn from a photograph by Ralph Morse in *The Primates;* © 1965 Time Inc. 3.5 From Jane van Lawick-Goodall, *In the Shadow of Man.* Copyright © 1971 by Hugo and Jane van Lawick-Goodall. Reprinted by permission of Houghton Mifflin Company. 3.6 Adapted from W. E. Le Gros Clark, *Fossil Evidence for Human Evolution* (Chicago: The University of Chicago Press); copyright © 1955 The University of Chicago.

Chapter 4: 4.1 Jerry Cooke, *LIFE* Magazine; © 1949 Time Inc. 4.2 Adapted from J. T. Robinson, "Adaptive Radiation in the Australopithecines and the Origin of Man," *Viking Fund Publications in Anthropology* #36, *African Ecology and Human Evolution,* edited by F. Clark Howell and François Bourlière, by permission of Aldine Publishing Company. Copyright by Wenner-Gren Foundation for Anthropological Research. 4.4 Adapted from W. E. Le Gros Clark, *Fossil Evidence for Human Evolution* (Chicago: The University of Chicago Press); copyright © 1955 The University of Chicago. 4.5 J. Desmond Clark. 4.6 From "Hominid Fossils from the Area East of Lake Rudolf, Kenya: Photographs and a Commentary on Context" by Richard E. Leakey and Glynn Ll. Isaac, in *Perspectives on Human Evolution 2,* edited by S. L. Washburn and Phyllis Dolhinow. Copyright © 1972 by Holt, Rinehart and Winston, Inc. Reproduced by permission of Holt, Rinehart and Winston, Inc.

Chapter 5: From *Prehistory of Africa* by J. Desmond Clark (London: Thames and Hudson, 1970), by permission of the publisher. 5.2 S. L. Washburn. 5.3 Adapted from *The Primates;* © 1965 Time Inc. 5.4, 5.5, and 5.6 From Jane van Lawick-Goodall, *In the Shadow of Man.* Copyright © 1971 by Hugo and Jane van Lawick-Goodall. Reprinted by permission of Houghton Mifflin Company.

Chapter 6: 6.2 Adapted from W. E. Le Gros Clark, *The Antecedents of Man: An Introduction to the Evolution of the Primates* (Chicago: Quadrangle Books). 6.3 Adapted from J. T. Robinson, "Adaptive Radiation in the Australopithecines and the Origin of Man," *Viking Fund Publications in Anthropology* #36, *African Ecology and Human Evolution,* edited by F. Clark Howell and François Bourlière, by permission of Aldine Publishing Company. Copyright by Wenner-Gren Foundation for An-

Preface

Over the last few years major advances have been made in the study of human evolution, including (1) advances in molecular biology and immunochemistry which settle many of the controversies over the relationships of man; (2) field studies which tell us more about what our nearest relatives are like; and (3) the discovery of fossils which give a much fuller description of the past. Methods for dating rocks have been improved, so the ages of fossils may be more accurately determined.

The purpose of this book is to give the reader a glimpse of this changing view of man and of his relationships to his predecessors. Some history is included to keep the changes in perspective. To simplify, the contributions of a few people are stressed, which we hope will make the story clear and interesting. The whole problem, however, is embedded in a climate of opinion, in a complex intellectual history. We have tried to sample in a way that simplifies and keeps the meaning as correct as it would be with a much longer and more complicated approach.

The book is based on conversations between the authors, a mutually satisfactory outline, and the joint use of many sources. One of us (SLW) is responsible for the scientific point of view and the other (RM) for the mode of presentation.

We have tried to start with the present. As we indicate in the first chapter, the development of methods which make the direct comparison of the genetic substances (DNA) of different animals possible marks the beginning of a new era in evolutionary studies. It can no longer be doubted that our nearest living relatives are the African apes — the chimpanzee and the gorilla. Until 1970, it may have been reasonable to hold other opinions, and competent scientists believed that man's closest living relatives were African apes, gibbons, Old World monkeys, New

World monkeys, tarsiers, or other prosimians, and that the time of separation of the human lineage was anywhere from 5 million to 50 million years ago. Molecular and immunochemical studies show that most controversies resulted from an inadequate fossil record and poorly understood anatomy. We have avoided discussing issues which are now only of historical interest.

The course of evolution has been determined by natural selection, that is, by the behaviors which led to survival. This is why this book stresses behaviors. There is no way to understand the process of evolution by studying fossils alone, particularly when the fossils are as fragmentary as is the case in the primates. The fossil bones were important when they were parts of living animals, when they were parts of the anatomy of successful survival.

But most anatomy is not preserved, and our understanding of the behavior of times long past can only be based on reconstructions. For this reason the study of the evolution of any particular group of animals cannot be a science. The subject matter is not available for direct study, but must be reconstructed. For example, language is certainly one of the most important of human behaviors, and speech is made possible by complex and uniquely human anatomy. But this anatomy leaves no traces in the bones, and the fossil record gives no direct evidence on the time of the origin of languages. The theory of natural selection forces us to view evolution as the history of populations adapting over time, as the history of behavioral success; but the behavior must be reconstructed on the basis of the fossils, of what is known of contemporary forms, and of experiments.

Evolution is biological history, and the determination of time scales is essential for historical understanding. Recently, radiometric methods have been applied to finding the age of many fossils important in the study of human evolution. Potassium changes to argon at a constant rate and this process starts at the time of a volcanic eruption. So, if fossils are associated with rock or ash of volcanic origin, their age can be determined. Probably some new dates will make it possible to bring the molecular and immunochemical data into agreement with the fossil record.

Until recently, it was believed that the Pliocene epoch began 12 million years ago, so any fossil in rocks older than Pliocene must have been more than 12 million years old. However, recent determinations suggest that the Pliocene may have begun less than 6 million years ago. The error in dating the Pliocene may be the principal reason why many paleontologists have thought a recent origin of man could not be reconciled with the "facts" of the fossil record. This issue is not yet settled, but each year more and more dates are determined by quantitative methods.

Just as the molecular approach is used to measure the distances between the living primates by objective quantitative methods, so the dates of the past are being determined with equal reliability. These methods set limits and build a framework within which the student of human evolution must work. Each year the limits become more definite and the framework more detailed. Discoveries will undoubtedly continue to be made — new research and additional fossils. Indeed, important data, which are consistent with the views in this text, have been published since this book was written. In this book we have tried to present the picture as it seems to us in 1973.

Contents

1

Only Once

It happened only once.

Only once in the three billion years that life has been astir on this planet did man evolve.

As life spread out of the seas and onto the land and into the air countless millions of living forms evolved. More than 1,500,000 species are believed to live in the world today. Some of this multitude are as tiny as the virus; some are as huge as the whale; some, like the cheetah, have achieved great speed; others have eagle vision; some have persisted through more than a billion years, while innumerable others have perished; the millions of the present inhabit the mountains, the plains, and the depths of the earth, the arctics and the jungles, the deserts and the wetlands.

All have many successful attributes for life on this small, varied planet, but out of the untold billions of individuals and the vast number of species of the past and present, only one evolved our large type of brain, only one our kind of upright posture, only one our gift for language, only one our self-consciousness and the human way of life. Only one became man — and only in the last 5 million to 10 million years did this happen.

That even one should have made the transition from lower animal to apeman to man was long regarded as inconceivable and impossible.

Until 1859 nearly all men believed, often as an article of religious faith, that the one who was so different from all the others was a special creation, a fair, vernal being who had been set down in the Garden of Eden at 7 o'clock in the morning in the year 4004 B.C. Lucas Cranach the Elder painted the idyllic scene — Adam and Eve, perfect and unsullied, standing beneath the laden apple tree, while the gentle creatures of the earth, lambs, deer, and dogs, gamboled at their feet.

This ordained view of man's origin was abruptly challenged on November 24, 1859, when Charles Darwin published his *Origin of Species*. Though he made only one guarded reference to man as such, he demonstrated with nearly incontrovertible thoroughness that all life had descended from one beginning, and ultimately from one primordial cell. The implication was inescapable. Man, as part of Nature, had descended from some earlier, unquestionably animal stock. Angry and shocked critics leaped to the point, and charged that Darwin was proposing apes as man's ancestors. Twelve years later in *Descent of Man*, Darwin faced the question and said outright that "man is an offshoot of the Old World Simian stem."

The allegation that man, with his special standing and uniqueness, was descended from a crude, hairy creature swinging in the trees of Africa, outraged much of the world. Darwin was accused of "brutalizing humanity and sinking mankind to a lower grade of degradation than any into

4

which it has fallen since its written records tell us of its history."[1]*

Darwin could only answer that man ought frankly to admit his community of descent: "It is only our natural prejudice and arrogance which made our forefathers declare that they were descended from demi-gods."

Even those who were willing to listen demanded proof. There stood the apes — here stood man. Obviously they were different. If they were related, where were the forms in between them? Where were the missing links?

A few years before — in 1856 — workmen digging in the Neanderthal river valley in Germany had come upon an exceedingly odd skull. The heavy brow ridges and thick cranial bones were unlike those of any living man. Rudolf Virchow, the leading pathologist of the nineteenth century, held that the skull was an abnormal specimen. It had belonged, another expert declared, "to an individual affected with idiocy and rickets."

Darwin took no position, but his friend and defender, Thomas H. Huxley, made a thorough study of the puzzling skull, and noted: "We meet with ape-like characters, stamping it as the most pithecoid [apelike] skull yet discovered." He hastened to caution: "In no sense can the Neanderthal bones be regarded as the remains of a human being intermediate between men and apes." The controversy was enough, however, to lead German scientist Ernst Heinrich Haeckel to hypothesize that a half-ape, half-human creature might have existed somewhere, sometime, and to suggest that if it should ever be found, an appropriate name would be *Pithecanthropus erectus* (upright apeman).

A young Dutch physician, Eugène Dubois, whose imagination had been fired by the whole issue, wangled a government appointment in Sumatra to put himself in a position to take up the search. He reasoned that the chance might be good in an area where the orangutan — in Malay the name meant "forest man" — still survived. Several years

* The footnotes for the text appear at the back of the book starting on page 189.

later, in 1890, on the banks of a sleepy Java river, Dubois found the fossil his scientific imagination had visualized. There was a low, apelike skull, but nearby and seemingly belonging to the same being, he unearthed a humanlike thigh bone.

"I considered it a link between apes and men," said Dubois, and he named his discovery *Pithecanthropus erectus*. For those unwilling to admit any relation between apes and men, it was raw provocation. The denunciations were furious.

A few years later, in 1927, a Canadian physician, Dr. Davidson Black, found similar fossils in ancient cave deposits near Peking, China. Along with the bones were skillfully made tools and hearths on which these early men — not in-between creatures — had cooked their game.

Nevertheless, skepticism met the announcement in 1925 that a true "missing link," a creature with a skull very like that of an ape, yet with a human body, had been found in South Africa. Dr. Raymond A. Dart discovered the skull of a six-year-old child when he opened a box of fossilized bones that had been sent to him from a quarry at Taung. The skull was very small, no higher than that of a living ape, but the teeth proved to be essentially human. He named the child *Australopithecus* (south ape). Scientists were the dubious and the rejectors this time. But Dart and Dr. Robert Broom, a Scottish physician who had gone to South Africa to search for the fossil record of the mammals, continued their work.

Find succeeded find, both in South Africa and in East Africa where Mary and Louis S. B. Leakey explored the fossil-rich deposits of Olduvai Gorge. From former camp-sites along lakes of some millions of years ago and from the caves that had offered shelter, came adult skulls, pelvic bones that testified to an upright posture, a foot, a hand, hundreds of teeth, and thousands of stones simply chipped into tools for cutting and, perhaps, for killing. Exacting studies were made of all this yield from the past. The confirmation was complete and beyond all scientific doubt. The African creatures being unearthed had brains no larger than those of the apes. They had walked and run like humans. The foot differed little from that of modern man, and the hand was halfway to human conformation. The australopithecines had been tool-users, toolmakers, and hunters for a period that had extended over at least 3 million years, and they evidently had spread to other reachable parts of the world.

Later discoveries of australopithecine remains, made along the Omo River in Ethiopia, could be dated by analysis of radioactive potassium-argon back to more than 3 million years. Other finds indicated that the australopithecines might go back to more than 4 million years.

In almost exactly a century, the record the world had demanded of Darwin largely had been compiled. It went back to more remote times than almost anyone had deemed possible, and many missing links had been found. With the aid of the fossils man could see what he had been along most of the way: some 4,000,000 or more years ago an unexpected and odd combination with a brain no larger than an ape's and a humanlike body, but still probably a human leading an essentially human life; about 1,000,000 years ago, a larger-brained human who had mastered the use of fire and who made complex stone tools; and by 40,000 years ago, a virtually modern man. The record still was fragmentary, but it was complete enough to prove that man had evolved. The famous French scientist Georges Cuvier once had proclaimed: "L'homme fossile n'existe pas" — there's no such thing as fossil man. He and most of the world had been wrong.

But even the most primitive australopithecine was not an ape. His bones, his teeth — he had lost the big fighting canine fangs of the apes — his tools, and his hunting way of life all made this clear. In addition, all of his fossilized remains were found on the dry savannas to which his life was adapted. No remains have turned up in the forests which the apes inhabit. The South African australopithecines had lived far from the nearest jungles. The australopithecines were something new and different in the world.

The big questions then arose. Who had preceded them? Who were their ancestors and thus the ancestors of man. From what stock did they spring? Directly from the apes, as Darwin surmised?

Before the australopithecines, the fossil evidence is relatively meager. So far only a few hundred teeth and a few fragmentary skulls have been found of apes that show non-ape or humanlike characteristics and thus perhaps were moving in the direction of the australopithecines and man.

This all too scant material can be studied by comparative anatomy. It can be compared with the bones of modern apes, australopithecines, and man. Although the likenesses and differences testify somewhat to relationships and descent, the evidence is also ambiguous. Many interpretations of any of the fossilized bones are possible, and with insufficient fossils to correct the ambiguities the authorities differ widely about the early way to man.

Under the circumstances during the last half-century many scholars turned away from the Darwin-Huxley theory that man had descended directly from some earlier ape. Many maintained then and do now that the human lineage separated far in the past from some unspecialized primate, such as the little four-legged tarsier, or from some monkey. If that were the point of separation, it must have occurred far in the past, probably at least 30 million years ago. Others set the time of man's branching off from 5 million to 50 million years ago.

This last number is almost the duration of the age of mammals!

In truth, the great question of how and why man became man — of how lower animal turned into australopithecine — was mostly unanswerable, or at least answers were not certain.

Even recently, with the discovery of additional fossils and with the accumulation of an immense amount of information about the contemporary primates, no agreement could be reached about the origin of man. Respected paleontologists still arrived at widely differing estimates of time.

Figure 1.1. *There were many kinds of early primates, of which a few, very diverse forms survive: a loris (top), a slow-moving creature; a tarsier (bottom, right, a rapid-moving leaper; and two lemurs (bottom, left), creatures who have changed remarkably little through many millions of years.*

The continuing problem was that the fossils were and are fragmentary and that still no consensus could be reached on the interpretation of the data from comparative anatomy. There always were variations that made possible, or even forced, varied theories.

All the related questions also remained:

How, as well as when, did the separation from the predecessor come about?

How did a tree-living ancestor come down to the ground?

How were the canine fangs lost?

How did a four-legged ancestor become a biped?

How did the first apes to descend from the trees manage to survive on the ground?

How did animals that could only poke with a stick learn to use tools?

How was a move made from the forest to the savannah?

How did hunting and the social organization that had to go with it develop?

What happened to the brain and how did it ultimately, by the time of modern man, triple in size?

Why did these changes come about, and why did only one animal out of the millions evolve into *Homo*?

Most answers had to await development of objective scientific methods in which the role of personal opinion could be reduced. This is particularly true in the case of man, where emotion and conviction have been so strong.

Only lately, and unexpectedly, were such methods discovered. They opened new ways, with new precision, into areas that had seemed forever blocked or closed to the older methods.

First were discoveries in biochemistry, particularly in molecular biology and genetics. It was found that the hereditary material of life itself bore the record of evolution, and that this record was decipherable. Second, and at about the same time, another advance in the study of man's

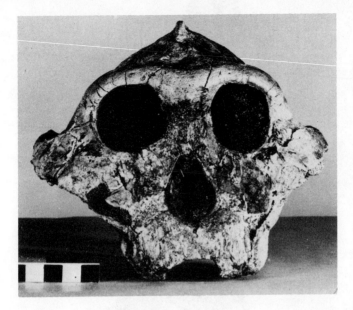

Figure 1.2. *A skull of fossil man* (Australopithecus) *found by Richard E. Leakey in the area east of Lake Rudolph, Kenya. The scale shown is in centimeters.*

origins was made possible by new kinds of field studies of animals in their native habitats. Further development of existing methods of timing the past, more fossil finds, and advances in comparative anatomy also illuminated much that had always been obscure. As it does in a few rare moments, the science of man made a large move forward in the 1960's and 1970's.

Man at last could identify and generally time his own evolution. His own immediate ancestry and his relations to other species could be traced. It became clear that man and the chimpanzees had parted evolutionary company a mere 5 million to 10 million years ago. The chimpanzees were established as our closest relatives — so close that in some parts of the body there are no differences at all.

11

Figure 1.3. *The swamp monkey, sitting on the branch, contrasts with the chimpanzee, with her baby on her back, knuckle-walking on the ground. The monkey's pattern of quadrupedal locomotion is primitive, whereas the ape's is specialized.*

Man and chimpanzee proved to be as close as sheep and goat, two species that had always been regarded as very close. Man and chimpanzee are more closely related than horse and donkey, cape buffalo and water buffalo, cat and lion, or dog and fox. Thus we are much nearer to the chimpanzees than to the monkeys many had believed to be our immediate ancestors.

Most notably this identification and change in the generally accepted order of evolution did not rest on opinion or interpretation. It was based instead on measurable, countable differences. Regardless of who performed the tests, or in what laboratories they were made, the results were exact and the same.

Some of the first experiments and counts were of DNA — deoxyribonucleic acid — which several decades before had been proved to be the bearer of all heredity and consequently the determinant of all living form. Its double strands, joined together by a varying order of chemical bases, structurally were very much like a spiral staircase. The two strands of DNA, however, separate and a new strand is formed on the template of the original strand to produce new DNA.

Also, the two strands of DNA could be made to separate in the laboratory. After separating the double strands of human and other animal DNA, the molecular biologists carrying on the new studies mixed the separated strands together and heated the mixture. The strands began to reassociate. In part the chimpanzee DNA strands fitted to the human strands; they went together almost like the pieces in a puzzle with only a 2.5 per cent difference in fit.

When single strands of monkey DNA were mixed with single human strands there was much less reassociation. The two were too much unlike to fit together closely. The difference was 10 per cent.

The laboratory techniques were much more difficult than this implies. But in this matching of like to like, B. H. Hoyer, David Kohne, and others saw the possibility of determining how near or how distantly related the various species might be. The first major application to the primates was published in 1970 and reached most scientists in 1971, just one hundred years after the publication of Darwin's *Descent of Man.*

A mass of futile effort and speculation would have been saved if molecular biology had been discovered 100 years sooner.

The close association of chimpanzee and human DNA, and the looser association of monkey DNA, said in unmistakable, quantitative, and verifiable terms that man and ape were much more closely related than man and monkey. DNA's fitted as well as they did because both had been inherited from the same ancestry, and that common ancestry was much nearer than the monkey ancestry. In the same way, children more closely resemble their parents than their great-great-grandparents.

The DNA matching technique was then further improved. Using it, Hoyer definitely identified the next nearest ancestor. It was the gorilla. The order was man, chimpanzee, gorilla. It meant that man and chimpanzee shared a common ancestor after the ancestors of today's gorilla had separated off in a line of their own.

The direct comparisons of DNA not only have shown that the African apes are our closest relatives, but which one is closest. The technique can also be used to demonstrate our distance from other animals and the relatedness of one to another. Many long-standing problems of classification of animals may soon be solved. The relation of man to the other primates has virtually been settled, and our own family genealogy is at last in order.

The discoveries that DNA made possible have made most of the earlier theories of human origin primarily of historical interest. The idea that man stemmed from the tarsiers or some other primitive mammal has been virtually demolished. And Darwin and Huxley, rather than most of their successors of the last century, have been proved right. Their reasoning, that the African apes were our nearest ancestors, is now supported by the new scientific determinations.

14

Before the discovery of DNA and even before the direct comparison of DNA's was possible, a start was made on another method of comparing living forms. DNA, as the basic shaper of all, determines the exact structure and order of the most basic of body chemicals, the proteins. The proteins, the substance of our blood, skin, and bones and much more, are composed of long chains of amino acids. It took Frederick Sanger twelve years in the 1940's and 1950's to work out the sequence of the 51 amino acids in the two chains of the protein insulin. Later many other proteins were similarly analyzed or mapped.

One was hemoglobin, the oxygen-carrying protein of the blood. Without it, no living thing could breathe or exist. It was soon learned that there are 141 amino acid units in the alpha hemoglobin chain and 146 in the beta — all

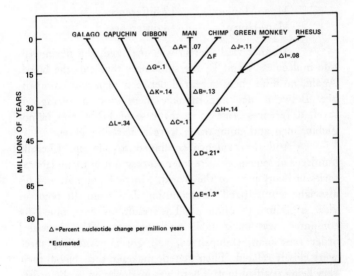

Figure 1.4. *A primate phylogenetic tree based on DNA divergence data, prepared by David E. Kohne. The chimpanzee and the gibbon (both apes) show the closest correlation to man, in that order; the two Old World monkeys, the green from Africa and the rhesus from India, come next; the capuchin, a New World monkey, has a lesser correlation still; and the galago, a prosimian from Africa, has the least of those shown.*

arranged like so many beads on a string. Scientists next were able to obtain the order of the units in the hemoglobin chains of man, chimpanzee, gorilla, monkey, horse, and several other animals.

Then one string could be compared with another. The results were startling:

Man–Chimpanzee:	No difference whatsoever. Each of the 287 amino acids in the two chains — 141 in one and 146 in the other — was the same and in the same place in the chain. The chains were, in effect, identical.
Man–Gorilla:	Only 2 differences, one in each chain.
Man–Monkey:	12 differences.
Man–Horse:	43 differences.[2]

Another vital protein was analyzed, the fibrinopeptide molecules A and B, the substances that clot the blood. Again, no differences appeared between man and chimpanzee. Between man and monkey there was an average of seven differences. Just as in the case of DNA and hemoglobin, man and chimpanzee were remarkably close.

And the evidence continued to pile up. Literally hundreds of sequences were later worked out in many laboratories in many parts of the world. Morris Goodman and his associates summarized the mounting data from the point of view of human evolution.[3] The result, as determined by computer, was indisputable and the same. The ancestral order ran: man, chimpanzee, and gorilla. And the three were closely related. Their genetic makeup, their blood, their very being testified to it. There was no deviation in the order.

Despite improvements in the technique, the development of sequences was slow and painstaking. Matsuda and associates in Japan worked for six years on the hemoglobin sequences in man and rhesus monkeys.

Within the last decade another and ultimately faster

process was developed. It had long been known that humans and other animals generally build up antibodies against foreign substances entering the blood. If human serum is injected into a rabbit, the rabbit will build up antihuman antibodies. Repeated injections strengthen them. Some blood may then be taken from the rabbit, and the serum used to test the serum of other animals. As the test serum is antihuman, the closer an animal is to man, the stronger the reaction will be.

As early as 1904, Nuttall had proposed that this method could be used to measure the true relationships between animals — outward appearances often are deceptive. During the next fifty years, however, the method was used only sporadically, and its possibilities generally were overlooked.

Only in the 1960's did the use of purified proteins rather than the whole serum demonstrate the real power of immunochemical methods. Scientists thus acquired a new-old tool of many possibilities and great exactitude.

Goodman and the workers in his laboratory are among the most active researchers in comparing the primates by immunochemical methods. Their results, based on computerized analyses of hundreds of tests, once again are striking. In distance units the primate order was confirmed once more:

Man	0.0	
Chimpanzee	0.2	
Gorilla	1.0	
Orangutan	2.2	
Gibbon	3.4	
Old World Monkey	4.0	(average of several)
New World Monkey	6.5	(average of several)
Prosimian	10.0	(average of several)
Tree Shrew	13.0[4]	

Though the figures may change slightly with continuing experiments on different proteins, the order is not expected to vary. It is believed to be established beyond fluctuation. "A large body of data demonstrate that man is more closely related to the African apes than to the Asiatic," Goodman wrote.

Still another new method added further confirmation. At the University of California, Berkeley, Allan C. Wilson and Vincent M. Sarich are studying proteins using immunochemical methods that permit precise measurements with very small amounts of antibody — the substance produced by the injected rabbits.

They first injected rabbits with human albumin, and tested the antihuman antibody they obtained against a wide variety of primates. The albumin results, like the serum results, were expressed in "immunological distance units," or ID units. Thousands of tests have been performed. They showed the following albumin distances between man, the apes, and the monkeys:

Man to Chimpanzee:	7 units
Man to Gorilla:	9 units
Man to Orangutan:	12 units
Man to Gibbon:	15 units
Man to Old World Monkey:	32 units
Man to New World Monkey:	58 units[5]

Wilson and Sarich also studied the albumin immunological distance between primates and nonprimates — represented in these tests by carnivores. From nonprimate to man the distance was 169 units.

The chimpanzee also was separated from the carnivores by the same 169 units, as were both the Old and New World monkeys. The data therefore not only recorded the distances separating the primates from the nonprimates, but indicated that after the primates parted company with the carnivores, all the primates continued to evolve in their separate ways at essentially the same rate. If the primates were compared to twigs growing out of the same branch, it could be seen that each twig attained about the same length.

Though the primates were evolving separately at the same rate, Wilson and Sarich found in their research that

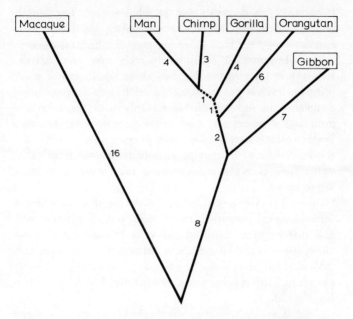

Distances man to: chimpanzee 7, gorilla 9, orangutan 12, gibbon 15, Old World monkey 32.

Figure 1.5. *An evolutionary tree based on immunological evidence using albumin immunological distance units. The precise figure will vary somewhat from experiment to experiment; the general proportions remain the same. The macaque is an Old World monkey.*

not all groups were evolving so rapidly. The lemur, a prosimian, was only 150 units distant from the carnivores; the tarsier, the prosimian often designated in the past as the most direct ancestor of man, was 163 units removed. Neither had come along as rapidly on its own course as the primates.

Evolution always has been pictured as a tree, but the tree with its trunk and its intricate pattern of branching is far more than a visually convenient representation of a process. It shows graphically all that has occurred in evolution and the scientist's theories of what groups have sprung

19

from which predecessors and at what points. The length of any branch also indicates his conclusions about how long any one group has been separated from its ancestral stem.

Innumerable evolutionary trees have been drawn, although in the past the decisions about where and at what point the various groups branched off had to depend on incomplete and inconclusive data. Only with the new immunological studies can some of the guesswork be removed. Insofar as the new studies have gone, it can now be determined where the groups branched off and from what stems. Some clues also are developing about when the branching occurred.

The Wilson-Sarich work showing that the albumin immunological distance between man and chimpanzee is 7 and that between man and gibbon is 15 indicates that the chimpanzee branched off about halfway between man and gibbon. That branch can be put into place with considerable assurance. And it is becoming abundantly clear which group begot which.

The new trees could be checked in a number of ways. The tree based on albumin differences and similarities could be checked against the tree based on DNA. The two agree, although the DNA tree still is incomplete. The albumin tree also agrees with the still partial trees being developed from the sequences of the amino acids. Further new studies with the transferrins, the iron-binding proteins of the blood plasma, offer still another check of the branching of the primate section of the evolutionary tree.

Transferrin tables prepared by Goodman showed the same evolutionary order, the same branching:

Man	0.0
Chimpanzee	0.0
Gorilla	0.0
Orangutan	2.7
Gibbon	2.7
Leaf Monkey	3.8
Macaque	3.8
New World Monkey	6.0
Prosimian	11.0[6]

The evidence of the closeness of man and the African apes and the relative distance of man and monkey thus accumulated with near inexorability. A summary shows its consistency and power:

DNA:	Man, chimpanzee, and gorilla nearly the same.
Hemoglobin and Fibrinopeptides:	Man and chimpanzee the same. Monkey different.
Albumin:	Similar constellations in man, chimpanzee, and gorilla; different constellation in monkey. Reactions to antibodies the same in man, chimpanzee, and gorilla; different in monkey. Immunological differences narrow between man, chimpanzee, and gorilla; wider between man, monkey, and other primates.
Transferrins:	The same evolutionary order indicated by other tests.

In no instance is the biological data contradictory, whether derived from studies of DNA, the proteins, or immunochemistry, or whether the studies were made in the United States, Europe, or Asia. The new work pointing to relationships that few were willing to grant during the last century meets the standards of scientific reliability.

Despite the sweep of the new data some scientists do not accept the usefulness of the molecular revolution. A book by one authority, Björn Kurtén, published in 1972, is titled *Not from the Apes*. Its author is one of the latest to argue that the human line must have separated from that leading to the apes more than 35 million years ago. He rejects the chemical information because it is "not historical."

The issue of man's relations to the apes still continues very much alive. The dispute also raises another question. If man and the African apes are biologically so close as to be nearly inseparable in many essentials, why do they look so different? No one could ever confuse a chimpanzee and a man. Nor man's face with what Darwin called "gorilla's frightful physiognomy." Scientific observers studying these differences and affinities, in addition to the fossil record, placed man in a family of which he was the sole member, the Hominidae. The African apes were usually placed with the rest of the apes in the family Pongidae.

Darwin had commented many years ago that if man had not been his own classifier, "he would never have thought of founding a separate order for his own reception." Nevertheless man is distinct, he is unique, and only he has evolved to anything like the human state.

How could the newly discovered inward likeness and the obvious outward difference be explained? Science could at last also explore the problem with the new biological means, and the search went back to the origins of life and to its long evolution as well as to the remarkable changes that finally made ape into man.

Evolution, it became increasingly clear, is a combination of relative unchangingness and change. Whether change or stability was to prevail depended initially upon where the change occurred.

From the beginning, when life was little more than a few cells made up largely of a few chains of protein, a mutation — a change, for example, in one out of possibly 300 amino acids in a protein chain — was likely to be fatal if it affected the primary functional activity of the protein. Any change at such an "active site" or section of the protein probably could not be tolerated. A new organism born with such a mutation generally could not function and died before it could produce offspring. That was the end of that particular change, and the vital section of the protein stayed very much the same in most descendants through millions and perhaps billions of years.

However, a mutation in another section of the protein might not upset the organism's functioning, and might in a few rare instances prove beneficial. Young organisms with a beneficial change had a better chance of surviving and reproducing. In these less vital areas change was possible.

The variability served well when the species spread

out into new environments. Perhaps a few individuals were sufficiently different to flourish in heat or cold or wetness or dryness. Out of this stock of variability and from the one or few individuals that were different arose many new species. Life spread from the seas to the land.

Man remained one species, despite his spread to all parts of the earth and even to outer space and the myriad differences in his appearance — color, hair, stature, and build. Science long has known that all men basically are alike under the skin. The new genetics and molecular biology includes the anthropoid apes in this category of internal likeness and outer difference. The visible, widely advertised differences are turning out to be outer and relatively recent.

When scientists studied apes and men in attempting to work out evolution, they generally studied the outer, the superficial differences. It was the same when the fossils were unearthed.

What the scientist saw in the fossil record is also mostly what one sees superficially — the small size of the brain, the large size of the face and the teeth, the long arms, and the characteristics of the feet. So the differences between men and the apes became those that might be found in the fossil record. What was inside — the blood, the heart, the liver, the arrangement of the internal organs, all the things that are almost identical — was not evident in fossils.

Two different classes of evidence thus developed. One was the sort of thing that appears to be true, and the other what is going on inside, something entirely different.

Outside, species are deceptively different looking. Inside, as it has now been shown, men are about as different from a chimpanzee as a chimpanzee is from a gorilla.

The reason is that the morphological things, the external things, the bones, the muscles, and so on, are what have recently changed. When we look at the differences between man and chimpanzee, we are looking at the results of our evolution. Many mistakenly thought that this must have taken a very long period of time.

Time was a key.

As scientists had studied the conspicuous external

23

differences between man and the other primates, they concluded that such differences must have taken a very long time to evolve. The majority arrived at the figures of from 25 million to 50 million years for the evolution of man.

But the new biological studies and the new view of evolution they make possible also allow a new timing of the process of evolution. Molecular biology has made it possible to determine the number of changes in the proteins and the quantity of change in the DNA. By counting the number of differences, the number of mutations can be estimated — that is, the genetic changes responsible for the observed differences, With differences counted and with an estimate of time from the fossil record, it then becomes possible to estimate the rate of change.

In hemoglobin, for example, there are 43 differences between man and horse. It is estimated that the two forms have been evolving independently for 150 million years, 75 million on the horse line and 75 million on the human line, since the two lineages diverged. This would indicate that one change occurred on the average of every 3 million to 4 million years. The calculation cannot be exact because some changes require more than one mutation, and there may be back mutations to an earlier order of amino acids. The time of separation must be based on a guess, though it is increasingly an informed guess.

Between gorilla and man there are two hemoglobin differences, and none between man and chimpanzee. The lack of differences between man and chimpanzee indicates that the two have not been separated long enough for a significant number of differences to accumulate. The 12 differences between man and monkey suggest that they have been separate for something of the order of 20 million to 25 million years.

The development of other sequences will provide other clocks to check the results of the study of hemoglobin. One such sequence is in the enzyme cytochrome *c*, which is important in respiration. Extensive studies indicate that changes occur in the enzyme at the rate of about one in 20 million years. Clearly what is needed to help in the problems of human evolution is a sequence or two which is changing at a much faster rate.

The study of immunochemical differences offers the possibility of much more useful evolutionary clocks. Sarich is developing one on the basis of changes in the albumins. He thinks that evolutionary rates may be calculated from immunological distances and that these can be conveniently measured in immunological distance units. This work, as noted earlier, has already shown that man, ape, and monkey have all changed nearly the same amount since the beginning of primate history. Only a firm date is needed to calibrate the evolutionary tree of the primates.

Unfortunately, the timing of every major event in primate evolution is under debate. There is no agreement when the primates separated from other mammals, when New and Old World monkeys separated, or when ape and monkey lines became separate. However these major events may ultimately be decided, all evidence suggests that the time of separation between man and the African apes must be small. There has not been enough time to accumulate any large amount of change in hemoglobin (none between man and chimpanzee!), or in any other protein studied to date.

Despite the lack of firm dates, the new molecular and immunological findings have set limits to the previously almost unlimited speculations. It is now clear that the rates of change in monkeys, apes, and men have been remarkably uniform. The amount of difference is, at least in a general way, proportional to time.

On this restricted, if not precise basis, Sarich estimates the time of separation of the African apes from the monkeys at about 24 million years ago. Similar calculations place the time of branching off of the human line at around 10 million years or less.

The fossil record shows that the australopithecines, those close relatives and predecessors, were alive more than 4 million years ago. So the range of the probable times of human origin is narrowed to between 5 million and 10 million years.

The absence of certain mutational changes also un-

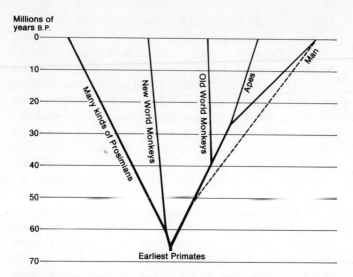

Figure 1.6. *A comparison of two views of primate evolution (a and b).*

a. A commonly held view of primate evolution. According to this view, the New World monkeys are derived from North American prosimians, and their similarities to Old World monkeys are due to parallel evolution. Man has a separate ancestry for some 25 million years, or, according to some individuals, for much longer than that (shown by the dotted line on the figure).

derwrites the recent date. If man had been separated from the chimpanzees for 20 million years as some maintain, five or six mutations should have been fixed in the hemoglobin. But there are none.

If the separation were 20 million years, the immunological differences should be large. The only ones that exist are small. The inescapable conclusion is that there has not been enough time for the expected mutations to occur and become fixed. Man's emergence is moved from the imposing past of 50 million, or even 20 million years, to something on the order of 5 to 10 million.

"Indeed," Sarich said, "our calculations indicate that it is difficult to seriously consider any date in excess of

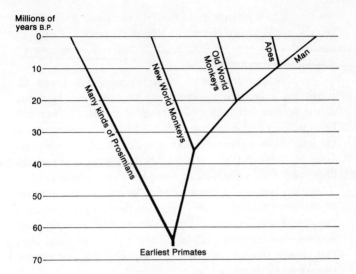

Millions of
years B.P.

b. A view of primate evolution as suggested in this book. This view of the primates differs from that shown opposite. New World and Old World monkeys have a long period of common ancestry after separating from primitive prosimians. The New World monkeys reached the New World, perhaps on rafts, crossing the sea from Africa some 35 to 40 million years ago, before the South American and African continents had drifted far apart. Man is shown separating from the African apes less than 10 million years ago, after sharing a long period of common ancestry with the apes.

10,000,000 years for the origin of the hominid lineage. A divergence time of 4,000,000 to 5,000,000 on the other hand is highly probable, according to the protein clock approach."[7]

It looks as though human evolution is a very recent event.

"Only" 5 million or 10 million years, the anthropologists exclaim with wonder. To the anthropologist 5 million years for man's emergence as man and his separation from ape ancestors is apt to seem only a moment in time. Set against the 3 billion years now given for the existence of life on earth, the human line becomes very young.

27

The layman is more likely to exclaim, "Five million years! . . . What an eternity." When 80 years is a ripe old age and a country of 300 years is believed mature, even 1,000,000 years has little meaning.

To put time in its proper perspective, James C. Rettie has originated an imaginary time scheme. Imagine, Rettie proposes, that the inhabitants of another planet had been making a continuous motion picture of the earth for the last 757 million years, with one picture taken each year. Imagine further that the film became available to earthlings, and that a continuous one-year show was arranged. Through January, February, and March, as the pictures of the earth flashed on the screen at the normal projection rate, there was no sign of life. Early in April though, little single-celled organisms began to appear in the seas and later that month some having many cells. The first vertebrates swam into view late in May.

It was the middle of July before any green appeared on the barren landscape. The first plants had started to grow and to open the way for animal life. Late in August the first amphibians were crawling out onto the shores. The reptiles did not follow until the middle of September. The mighty dinosaurs dominated the scene through the remainder of September, all of October, and part of November, for about seventy days in all.

In the meanwhile the first birds were fluttering heavily into the air and some furtive little mammals scurried through the underbrush. The rise of the Rocky Mountains toward the end of November brought the great era of the reptiles to a close.

The film ran on into December. The mammals became dominant and spread across the earth. Christmas arrived. The earthling audience was getting uneasy. There had been no sign of man. Day followed anxious day until December 31 and the last day of the showing. About noon the first primitive men appeared on the savannahs and the edges of the forests. During the afternoon the glaciers pushed southward and retreated four successive times, and

28

the little bands of men moved back and forth with them seeking their game in the wake of the ice.

About 11 P.M. men camped beside streams and lakes, could be seen chipping stone tools and a few minutes later they began to cultivate the soil. Five minutes before the end of the year came the dawn of civilization, and 1 minute and 17 seconds before the end of the film the beginning of the Christian era, 1 A.D. Twenty seconds before midnight Columbus discovered America, and in the last seven seconds the Declaration of Independence was signed. Only in the last split-second did man reach the moon.

Out of the entire year, man had been in existence for only 12 hours. The 5 million to 10 million years newly proposed for our evolution is truly only a fleet, brief moment in time.

In the last few years, new insights into what Darwin called "the constitution of man" have identified our ancestors as the apes and have set 5 million to 10 million years for the time that has made us distinctly man. Biological and chemical studies unexpectedly have revealed for the first time how man has changed or has not changed inwardly. Even the time of the change can be estimated.

Far less change than anticipated was required to convert ape into man, for in many aspects man remained essentially apelike. The obvious and well-known differences that so positively distinguished the two — their differences in appearance — came late in evolution. The similarities, the ancestral, hereditary similarities, tend to be hidden.

However great or small, the changes occurred only once. Only once out of untold millions of opportunities did man evolve.

2

Huxley Was Right

There was the great, seeming contradiction. Men and apes obviously were different. No one could possibly confuse the two. And yet the newest findings were showing that down deep the two were remarkably alike. Such a combination was as confounding as it had been generally unexpected at this time.

If the differences that were so obvious to the eye were only the finishing touches and the development of the last 5 million to 10 million years, and if the likenesses were the heritage from an earlier ancestry, then there was no contradiction. Outer difference and inner likeness were explainable.

Nevertheless, the problem was so complex and in

some parts so new and controversial that all possible evidence had to be found. The urgency led to new studies of the anatomy of men and apes.

Anatomy had been the first resource of those who set out to understand evolution. "It is notorious," Darwin wrote in *The Descent of Man* (1871), "that man is constructed on the same general type or model as other mammals. All the bones of his skeleton can be compared with corresponding bones in a monkey, bat, or seal. So it is with his muscles, nerves, blood vessels, and internal viscera. The brain, the most important of all organs, follows the same law."

Huxley, who made the bone-by-bone and muscle-by-muscle comparison, had concluded: "Whatever system of organs be studied, the comparisons of their modifications in the ape series leads to one and the same result — that the structural differences which separate Man from the Gorilla and the Chimpanzee are not so great as those which separate the Gorilla from the lower apes." The similarity of general structure had been evident long before biochemistry disclosed the molecular likeness.

The Complexes Compared

As the problem grew acute in the 1940's and 1950's, one author (S. L. Washburn) turned to the study of the big structural complexes of man and beast, because the functioning of the entire animal — not a single bone or group of bones — determined whether it survived or perished. The trunk and the arms comprised one such complex — essential for any animal that had lived in the trees. When compared, the same complex in man and apes was nearly the same.

The human trunk proved similar to that of an ape in length of arm, breadth of trunk, and shortness of the lumbar region. More detailed examination showed that the similarity extends to the sternum, length of clavicle, and many details of the bones, joints, and muscles.

In short, men and apes share major structural features of the trunk and the motions that these make possible, such as stretching to the side and hanging comfortably by one arm.

The finding was dramatically illustrated when a scale drawing of a man was cut in half down the center, and a similarly scaled half-drawing of an ape was placed beside it; the two trunks fitted together from thigh to shoulder almost as though they went together. If it had not been for the higher hunched shoulders of the ape, the fit of the body center would have been almost complete.

In the whole middle section of the body, men are

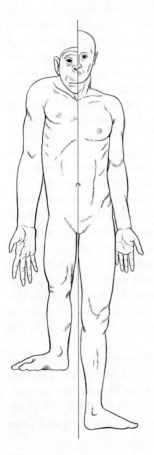

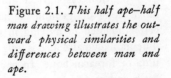

Figure 2.1. *This half ape—half man drawing illustrates the outward physical similarities and differences between man and ape.*

33

essentially the same as apes, or vice versa. The structure and musculature make it possible for both to move powerfully and habitually to the side and above. For the ape these are the movements for climbing and feeding. For the human they meet untold needs. To find out how essential a sidewise and upward reach are, students sometimes are asked not to reach for anything for an hour. That means not picking up a book from a desk, or a plate on a cafeteria line, or holding to a strap in a crowded bus. The ape reaches up to hold to a branch while he picks and eats some ripe fruit. The environment differs for humans, not the hold.

Both apes and men have a forearm capable of 180 degrees of rotation. Both thus can easily put the arm down flat on a table with the palm of the hand turned down, or with no conscious effort turn the arm around with the palm upward in the begging or supplicating position. The structure that both share also permits strong flexion or turning in either position — that is, a man can chin himself either with the palms of the hand turned toward him, or away from him, facing the bar. The monkey, in contrast to apes and men, does not have the same degree of rotation or similar power. Apes and men also have much freer movement of the wrist and elbow than does the monkey.

Monkeys also do not share an even more remarkable feature of the flexible ape arm — the stable position of the wrist in what the anatomist calls the "partially supinated position." It permits the chimpanzee and gorilla, and the human football lineman, to double under the ends of the fingers and rest part of the weight on the knuckles. The apes move very efficiently through the forest by knuckle-walking. The linesman uses the knuckles-down position as he prepares to charge the opposition. It gives him a fast getaway.

Monkeys have a different wrist joint. When they move along the ground the hand is put down flat. They are better adapted to moving in the trees than on the ground. The monkey palm also is long; it covers the distal end of the ulna or forearm bone. In ape and man this elongated palm has been lost.

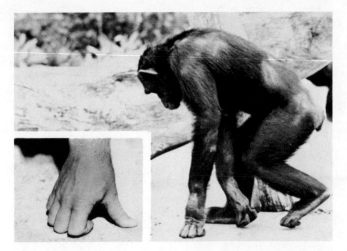

Figure 2.2. *The photographs of the chimpanzee and the human hand (inset) show the similarities between the chimpanzee knuckle-walking and the human hand in knuckle-walking position.*

A seeming oddity further underscores the likeness of man and ape. Neither has much hair on the backs of the fingers, and this relative baldness is under genetic control. Scientists formerly could not see any advantage in relative hairlessness of the finger backs, but it is this surface that bears the weight of the knuckle-walker. In chimpanzee and gorilla the skin of the second phalanx of the fingers is thick and hairless, a common development in any weight-bearing surface.

It may well be that this lack of mid-digital hair in man is at least a partial adaptation to knuckle-walking by our remote ancestors.

In summary, the structure of the human trunk and arms is remarkably apelike. It is this anatomical similarity that forms the basis for the actions that are similar in apes and men. Just as the motions in the living creatures are basically alike, so the structures are alike. The fact that anatomists have no difficulty in using an atlas of human anatomy when dissecting a chimpanzee arm clearly shows this.

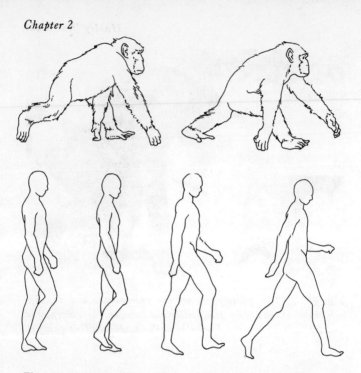

Figure 2.3. *A comparison of ape and human locomotion.*

A second great complex is made up of the legs, and here the differences between man and apes are striking. In the half-and-half comparison, illustrated on page 33, the human leg is 10 or 12 inches longer than that of its ape counterpart. A composite creature would walk with an impossible limp. Upon examination, bones, muscles, and functions of the lower legs of the two are easily distinguishable.

Neither ape nor any other animal walks like man, although there are many other bipeds. Birds, some dinosaurs, and pterodactyls evolved bipedal adaptations without freeing the hands for tool-using. Others also have evolved long legs. Tarsiers and gibbons, for example, have legs as long as man's relative to the trunk. But only man walks like man.

The structural basis for the human walk is complex. Initially it involved a new method of transferring the landing and balancing functions of fore limbs to the hind limbs. In the quadrupedal monkey or knuckle-walking chimpanzee, when the drive for a step comes from the right rear leg, the animal lands on the left fore limb. In man the foot has two functions to perform as it touches the ground: it must first do the landing and balancing and then it must give a push to produce the next step.

To make possible all of this and man's gravity-defying vertical position, the pelvic region had to change. The ilium, the upper part of the pelvis, became shortened in comparison to that of the apes. With related changes in the sacrum, a bony birth canal was completed. However, the shortening of the key ilium alone did not change the relation of the

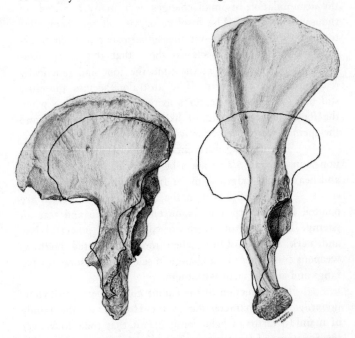

Figure 2.4. *A comparison of a human pelvic bone* (*left*) *with that of a chimpanzee* (*right*). *The outline of the same bone of* Australopithecus *has been superimposed on the others. Note how much closer the outline is to that of man's pelvic bone.*

37

trunk and legs and eliminate the stoop of the apes. For the backbone and trunk to become vertical a backward bend of the ilium also was necessary. Without still further changes though, the backward bend would have blocked the pelvic outlet and an animal born with such a change could not have produced offspring to carry it on. But other changes did occur. As the sacrum was moved up and out of the way of the birth canal and a curve was added to the lower backbone, the trunk became vertical. Some lesser changes also were necessary, but they also occurred. The result was that the knuckle-walking ape became upright and could walk in a new way. Literally a big step was taken toward man.

The actual course of evolution would have involved the accumulation of small changes over many hundreds of thousands of years. The fossil record is still too incomplete to supply information about the actual order of such transformations. But the fossils do show that this reorganization was not complete at the time the foot had practically reached its present form. The australopithecines therefore still had some apelike features in the pelvis at a time when the foot had become almost like that of modern man and the apemen were at least partly upright.

The next big difference in the half-and-half illustration is in the face. The ape's big muzzle, his massive jaw, and heavy brow ridges seem far from the human face.

The ape fights with the face. His canine teeth are pointed fangs, sharp and strong enough to rip and tear an enemy. The dangerous teeth are backed with powerful jaw and neck muscles. Only when tools supplanted teeth as weapons could there be a change in selective pressures for big fangs and all that went with them.

The reduction of the canine complex was an evolutionarily novel characteristic of the Hominidae, the family of man. In terms of behavior it meant that tools took over the functions of the teeth in protecting against predators, in fighting within the group, and in inter-group fighting. Man's ancestors thus lost their "frightful physiognomy" and took on the face that man regards as less brutal and more refined.

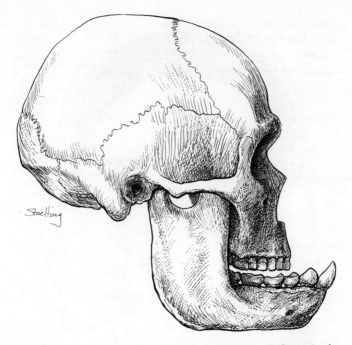

Figure 2.5. *This drawing combines the human skull with the jaws of an ape. Notice that the lower jaws of the ape project far beyond the upper teeth of the human skull; the teeth contrast as well, the ape's being larger and longer.*

The Biggest Difference

One more huge difference separates man from ape. In the half-and-half illustration, man's head rises much higher than the low flat skull of the ape. At the top the two halves do not match at all. The reason, of course, is that the human skull has been enlarged to house a larger brain.

The average human brain is about triple the size of the brain of the ape — some 1,200 to 1,500 cubic centimeters as compared to 400 to 600 cubic centimeters for the apes. Man's brain resembles the basic ape brain with several new areas added, areas that make man typically man because they are the areas that make possible hand skills, speech, mem-

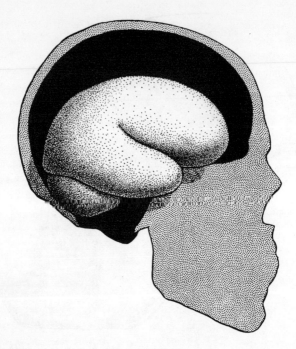

Figure 2.6. *The human skull housing an ape's brain; the black area indicates the space the human brain fills.*

ory, and the use of memory that involves conscious thought and planning.

The areas can be mapped almost as clearly as the geologist maps a continent, identifying each area and its extent. Surgeons as well as other scientists helped to map the brain. As they operated to remove growths or to repair other damage surgeons learned that certain areas produced certain responses. Gradually the brain as a whole was mapped. The brains of apes have similarly been marked out.

A large part of the motor cortex of the human brain governs hand movements. In a monkey the hand and foot areas of the brain are about equal in size, whereas in man the hand area greatly exceeds the foot area.

Part of the hand movements of both man and apes

are coordinated in the cerebellum, an area lying behind and below the brain, or cerebrum. The cerebellum in man is approximately three times that of an ape and the most enlarged part is that associated with learned hand movements.

Man also has a larger area of the brain used for language. The ape has only a small area for communication. Obviously the brain is essential for any act of communication but apparently very little brain is required in nonlinguistic communications systems. Any debate over the nature of the neural structures which make language possible should not confuse the fact that there are new parts of the brain which make language possible. Apes and monkeys cannot be taught to talk, although they can be conditioned to respond appropriately to sounds and even manual signs.

The monkey has nearly all the "design features," or the apparatus for speech, as scientists have demonstrated. What he lacks is the added brain that would make it possible.

In the low-browed, low-domed skull of the ape is a brain well provided with primary sensory and motor areas. There is nothing wrong with the ape's eyesight or hearing or agility. Man, in his turn has all of this, but more too. Therein lies the difference.

Behavior in the Wilds

The question nevertheless persisted. Are the apes of Africa today, the huge hulking gorilla and the hairy inquisitive chimpanzee, like any ancestral ape? Did man's ancestor once look like the apes in the wild, or like those in the zoo? Could studying the living apes supply any clues to the ancestral lines? Could a study of living apes tell man anything about himself?

Darwin and all evolutionists have emphasized that the living apes have evolved since the time — whatever it might be — when their ancestors and man's parted company. All conceded that change would have occurred. Only recently have new studies shown that behavioral change in the apes may have been relatively slight. Man's behavior was evolving and changing rapidly. The apes stayed generally the same.

Man was very slow to learn about his animal relatives. When the first accounts — generally sailors' tales — of the existence of manlike apes began to reach Europe, they smacked of the two-headed dragon variety. In *Purchas His Pilgrimage*, published in England in 1613, an old soldier who had lived in Africa for many years reported "a kinde of Great Apes, if they might bee so termed, of the height of a man, but twice as bigge in features of their limmes, with strength proportional, hairie all over, otherwise altogether like men and women in their whole bodily shape."

Drawings of the reputed "monsters" often resembled a human in a hairy suit. A tail was sometimes added. In 1699 though, the Royal Society published a memoir listing forty-seven points in which the "ourang-outang" "more resembled Man than Apes and Monkeys do," and thirty-four points in which it "differ'd from a Man and resembled more the Ape and Monkey kind."

Few were willing to undertake any kind of a systematic study in the field. As Huxley said in 1863, "the man

Figure 2.7. *An early drawing of a primate.*

who risks his life by even a short visit to the malarious shores of those regions [Africa and Asia] may be excused if he shrinks from facing the dangers of the interior . . . and contents himself with collecting and collating the more or less mythical reports . . . of natives." If the dangers of the interior did not discourage possible students of the interesting great apes, reports of their ferocity certainly did. When one investigator went to Africa in 1896 to study the gorilla he built himself an iron cage in the forest and sat there day after day waiting for the gorillas to appear. Needless to say they did not.

A few studies got under way before World War II, but the rush to study the apes in their habitat started in the 1950's. The time was ripe, and investigators from Japan, England, France, Switzerland, and the United States launched field studies of the behavior of a variety of primates. At last some of the answers to evolution were to be sought in animals living as man's ancestors must have lived in the forests of the past.

By the end of the 1960's more than twenty studies were reported, most based on at least a thousand hours of close observation, and some, like Jane van Lawick-Goodall's, on continuing years of work.[1]

Jane Goodall is a tall, blonde English girl who grew up loving animals. She left school at 18 and worked as a secretary until she could go to Africa to study animals in the wild. Soon after she arrived in Nairobi, Kenya, in 1957, she met Leakey. When she told him of her interest, he suggested that she start by working for the Coryndon Museum of Natural History in Nairobi. For a while she served as Leakey's secretary. Later she accompanied Mary and Louis Leakey to the dig at Olduvai Gorge. Day after day they worked, sprawled out on the ground or on hands and knees, picking at the rock face with dental probes in the search for early man. The Leakeys' Dalmatians stood guard, for rhinos often wandered in to the site, and at night the burning eyes of the lions could be seen around the camp. In the evenings, nevertheless, Jane explored the countryside, on foot and unarmed, to watch the giraffes and the lions.

When Leakey became convinced that Jane's interest in animals was not a passing fancy, he suggested that she study the behavior of chimpanzees, and assisted her in getting a grant from the Wilkie Foundation to start the work.

Jane, accompanied by her mother, arrived at the Gombe Stream Reserve in June, 1960. Mrs. Goodall had volunteered to go along when the African authorities had refused to let a pretty young girl live alone in the bush.

Jane climbed through the forest, searching for the chimpanzees she had come to study. The sharp edges of the high grass cut her skin, and more than once she became tangled in underbrush that she learned later was simply impenetrable.

But the chimpanzees that she was braving this forest to study, fled the moment she approached. She could only hear them calling from afar. "I often returned to the camp in utter discouragement," she said. "Was my whole attempt doomed to failure?"

Two months later the chimpanzees still were keeping their distance, and both women fell ill with fevers that sent their temperatures soaring, her mother's to 105 degrees for five days. They had been assured that there was no malaria in the area, and had brought no medicine for it. Their cook Dominic, the only assistant they had employed, watched over them as best he could, and brought them tender omelets that they could not eat.

The illness, though, marked a turning point. As Jane recovered, she weakly climbed to a peak about 1,000 feet above the lake level. As she sat there, exhausted by her efforts, she heard chimpanzees in the trees just below her. They were feeding on ripening figs. Jane returned to her vantage point the next day, and the chimps came back to their figs.

Dressed generally in a green shirt and white shorts, and with her shoulder-length hair tied back with a ribbon at the neck, she must have seemed a very odd intruder to the chimpanzees. But she sat very still, and gradually the chimpanzees began to accept her. They no longer fled when they caught sight of her. Almost too happy to breathe, Jane began to make notes on their feeding behavior, the changing composition of the groups, and their habits of nesting in the trees each night.

By the time the fig season ended, about four weeks later, Jane could sit close enough to watch the chimpanzees without binoculars. They became individuals to her — Flo with the torn ears and ugly face and her infant daughter Fifi and her adolescent sons Figan and Faben; handsome David Graybeard with his white beard and gentle disposition; Leakey, well-built and rugged just like his namesake; J. B., for John Bull, and many others.

In about four months the young investigator knew the 15 miles of rugged country the chimpanzees frequented. Her skin had toughened to the cutting of the sword grass, and she no longer became entangled in the underbrush.

One morning as she headed toward the peak, she came upon David Graybeard trimming the edges from a wide blade of sword grass. He then poked his cleaned rod down a hole he had scratched in a large, domed termite nest. He waited a few minutes. Then he skillfully pulled out his rod and delicately licked it with his lips. He was termite fishing! When his first fishing rod weakened, he picked a piece of vine, stripped off its leaves, and continued his successful pursuit. Every now and then he would put his ear to the nest, listen carefully, and then scratch a new fishing hole. (Jane learned later that only in certain seasons do the termites make tunnels out to the surface. Until the time comes for a nuptial flight away from the nest, they keep the surface sealed with a thin cover of clay. When the chimps discovered and opened the tunnels, the termites re-sealed them as quickly as possible.)

That night Jane rushed excitedly into the camp to tell her mother "Some wild animals can *use* objects as tools. But David didn't simply use tools, he actually *made* them."

Figure 2.8. *Jane van Lawick-Goodall observed chimpanzees using tools — grass blades, twigs, and vines — to catch termites, a favorite food.*

"That means," said Mrs. Goodall with an excitement matching her daughter's, and with immediate understanding, "that man isn't the only toolmaker at all."

In her first year of work, Jane Goodall had made a finding of major importance. In the past man often had been defined as the "toolmaker." It was the supposed critical difference that set him apart from all other animals.

As Jane Goodall's and other work confirmed, the definition would have to be redrafted. Man was redefined as the one who can make tools to a set and predetermined pattern.

Two years later Jane Goodall was sitting on the verandah of her tent, working at a table, when she saw David Graybeard enter the clearing. With complete composure he climbed one of the palm trees and feasted on some of the ripe nuts. As he came down after a while he walked straight toward her. About five feet away he paused and his hair rose in the bristling effect that denotes any kind of excitement. Jane sat still. Suddenly he rushed forward and gently took a banana lying on her table.

Jane had her clue. After that she supplied bananas. Gradually many of the chimpanzees came daily for their favorite fare. To prevent the big males from gobbling everything — David had been known to eat sixty bananas at a sitting — and to insure a share for all, the fruit was distributed around the grounds in separate boxes. The chimps, though, were not going to wait until the time came for feeding and observation. They either tore the boxes apart or took them apart. They pulled pegs, opened catches, and yanked cords. Jane finally had to resort to concrete boxes with steel lids, controlled by wires threaded through an underground pipe. For a short time she was ahead. Then some chimp youngsters learned how to pull out the pins that held the lids. When bolts were substituted, they soon unscrewed them. Jane had to turn to electrically operated box lids. Again she was ahead of the ingenious chimps, though she felt quite certain that they would catch up once more.

The feeding gave her an unequalled observation post. From it she and the young Dutch animal photographer she had married, Baron Hugo van Lawick, watched Flo raise her newest baby, Flint. Maternal care, object manipulation, and group and individual relationships could be studied here in detail as well as in the forest. Many new insights into the roots of human behavior were gained. The roots definitely were there.

Studies of the Gorilla

George Schaller was a graduate student in zoology at the University of Wisconsin when one of his professors one day leaned back in his chair and asked: "How would you like to study gorillas?" Two years later Schaller was in Africa, in the Congo, climbing the slopes of Mount Karisimbu. As he and a guide followed a trail of broken branches and tramped grass left by a group of gorillas, his guide muttered constantly, "Gorilla kill you." Suddenly Schaller heard a rapid "Pok pok-pok." A gorilla was beating its chest.

In a short distance they came within sight of an adult male, sitting among the shrubs and vines. He was easily identifiable by his huge size and his silver gray back. Beside him sat a juvenile and three females, "fat and placid with sagging breasts and long nipples." Up in the fork of a tree was a female with a small infant clinging to the hair on her shoulders.

"I was little prepared for the beauty of the beasts before me," said Schaller in his book *The Year of the Gorilla*.[2] "Their hair was not merely black, but a shining blue black, and the faces shone as if polished."

Schaller and the gorillas sat watching each other. The big male rose repeatedly to his full height of about six feet, to beat a rapid tatoo on his bare chest and then would sit down again. After a time the group walked quietly away. There was none of the fabled ferocity of which Schaller had been warned.

Later, as the gorillas came to accept him to some degree, he met one group that he had identified and come to know individually. Mr. Crest, the leader, was both excitable and bold. Schaller discreetly climbed on a horizontal branch about five feet above the ground to watch the gorillas feeding and resting about a hundred feet away. At first they did not notice him. About an hour and a half later Mr. Crest spied him. The gorilla jerked up his chest and roared. With the others following their leader, Mr.

Crest advanced until he was within thirty feet of his observer. He halted there, but a female with an infant clutched to her chest angled nearer. She reached up and gave Schaller's branch a sharp jerk. Schaller held on and held his breath. The gorilla pulled herself up on the branch beside him.

> Both of us squatted on the limb, casting fleeting looks at each other like a pair of strangers on a park bench. [Schaller had learned that the gorilla does not like an obvious direct stare.] Having satisfied her curiosity the female gorilla swung down and her place was taken by a juvenile who between glances in my direction, bit off pieces of bark, seemingly out of nervousness. Interest in me then waned, and the group retreated to its former rest area, where it continued its daily routine as though I did not exist.

The gorilla, the frequent horrendous symbol of brutishness, then could be studied. The fierceness proved a myth. Schaller admitted that his own hair never failed to rise when he heard the shattering roar of a big silver back, but he soon learned that the blood-curdling sound and the huge rearing body largely were bluff. The hurtling bulk nearly always stopped before coming in contact with an opponent. "Gorillas are eminently gentle and amiable creatures," Schaller wrote. "Peaceful coexistence is their way of life."

Schaller's observations also disclosed that gorillas have strong attachments to members of their own groups. When groups met as they ranged through the forest on their daily rounds, each tended to stay together, but did not fight over territory: "The gorilla certainly shares its range and its abundant food resources with others of its kind, disdaining all claims to a plot of land of its own."

The gorillas spent from 80 to 90 per cent of their waking hours on the ground. They were not primarily arboreal, as most accounts had indicated. When they did climb trees, generally to sun themselves or sometimes to make a nest, their actions were slow and deliberate. Schaller compared their climbing ability to that of a ten-year-old boy.

As the gorillas moved along the forest floor, they walked with the knuckles down, often in a procession led by a silver-backed male, and brought up at the rear by a black-backed, younger male. The females and young generally were in between. Often the troop traveled from 1,000 to 2,100 feet a day in their 10–15 mile range. They did not return at night to a home base. "In some respects, gorillas might be considered nomads," Schaller wrote, "moving along and feeding, and finally bedding down whenever darkness overtakes them, only to begin another day of wandering."

The Past Way of Life

The field studies built up information on many other primates in addition to the chimpanzees and gorillas, on their characteristics, their individual and social behavior. It was, as Phyllis Jay of the University of California and editor of *Primates — Studies in Adaptation and Variability*, noted, "a glimpse into what may have occurred as man evolved into man."

> A great deal can be learned from the bones that comprise our fossil records, but the life of ancient primates comprised much more than the obvious function of these boney parts. For example, a certain kind of roughened surface on a fossilized ischium [the seat] merely indicates that the primate has ischial callosities. But by looking at how living primates with these callosities behave it is possible to infer that in all likelihood the ancient animal slept sitting up rather than on its side in a nest. This may seem trivial, but when many such clues are gathered and collated, the total picture of an animal's way of life fills in to a closer approximation of what it must have been.
>
> Our ancestors were not the same as the living primates, but the rich variability of behavior of modern monkeys and apes makes it possible to reconstruct the most probable pattern of related forms in the past.[3]

The studies of animals in their habitats already are making these suggestions about what life probably was for man's ancestors:

1. It was social. All monkeys and apes live in social groups. This aspect of behavior seems to be deeply rooted in the past.

2. It was restricted to an area. The primates today occupy limited ranges, closely coordinated with food, water, and escape routes. The land they use varies from a few acres for gibbons to an intermediate few square miles for chimpanzees and gorillas to more than fifteen square miles for savanna-living baboons. The implication is that as long as our ancestors were apes they also were restricted to narrow ranges. By the time they became hunters and roamed over hundreds of miles they had become humans.

3. In many species of monkeys and apes the female is sexually receptive only during relatively brief periods of time. Loss of the estrus cycle in humans may have provided an evolutionary advantage by reducing the fighting and tension that the sexual cycle often produces in nonhuman primates. The change from cycle to continuing sexual receptivity also may have produced a calmer development period for the infant. Jay comments that the studies of animals show the advantage of the change in controlling rage and sex. A small family group also generally is impossible with estrus behavior.

4. In the wild, monkeys do not manipulate objects except to display antagonism — then they may brandish a stick. Chimpanzees not only make tools for termite fishing, but wipe themselves dry with leaves, chew leaves into "sponges" for soaking up water in small inaccessible pools, and throw stones. Chimps, gorillas, and orangutans scream, throw branches, jump and run in angry display. The thrown objects are not accurately aimed, but are likely to be impressive and frightening, to the victim. If an opponent were accidentally hit during such a display, the "acting out" animal may have won the dispute, and such discoveries could have led to the evolution of tool use.

"In summary, the outstanding difference between human and nonhuman use of tools is *skill* and the biology that makes skill possible," said Jay. "Many primates use tools, but only a few species, apes and men, use tools as objects in agonistic display."[4]

All observers also have pointed out the importance of play among young nonhuman primates. It is how they learn the behavior that will be required of them as adults. The play behavior of chimpanzees and gorillas is remarkably more complex than that of monkeys.

"Surely it is more than a coincidence that [the chimpanzee] the nonhuman primate taxonomically closest to man is, according to many investigators, also the most manipulative, exploratory, and similar to man in play," Jay wrote. "The range of variation in play forms and games among chimpanzees is second only to man."

The young apes spend much of their time playing, running, and tumbling, clambering over adults, swishing branches and vines, and even rolling and using hard round fruit as balls. Nearly all monkey play, though, is wrestling and chasing. There is relatively little play with objects.

The new studies demonstrate that the social and individual habits of apes are much more like humans' habits than those of monkeys. Much of the base of human behavior is evident in these studies of apes in their natural environment. Much of it carried over. Where man departs from the behavior of the living primates and from the probable behavior of his ancestors, as in his skilled use of tools and his wider range, the departure came late. It was the added something that made him human. The animal studies, the days and years spent quietly in the forests watching the animals, added confirmation to the other work indicating that the development of man principally came late, in the last 5 million to 10 million years.

From Ape to Australopithecine

One species did not stop and another start. It was not like that at all. Over some millions of years, some early

Figure 2.9. *Faben, Figan, and Fifi play around Flo and Flint. These chimpanzees and others whose photographs appear in the rest of this book were observed by Jane van Lawick-Goodall and photographed by Hugo van Lawick.*

primate populations which may have ranged over much of Africa and Asia developed a few human or humanlike characteristics. And then a few more.

Before the australopithecines however, the fossil record is too incomplete to permit many certainties. No one

53

can say positively which of the changing apes were in the direct line to the australopithecines. Fossil apes with varying characteristics have been found in Europe, Africa, and Asia.

Far back in time, in the distant reaches that are nearly incomprehensible to man, forests covered most of Africa, Asia, and Europe. The continents were joined at many points and there were no geographic barriers to the movement of apes. One genus might extend from Africa to India, a range indeed not greater than that occupied today by *Cercopithecus aethiopia*, or vervet. And one or more did.

The fossilized teeth and a few other scraps of the bones of prehuman primates have been recovered from sites in Spain, France, Kenya, Uganda, Turkey, Georgia, the U.S.S.R., Egypt, India, Pakistan, and China. Elwyn L. Simons of Yale University estimates that the number of specimens may now total about 550.

Some of the Finds

About sixty miles southwest of Cairo where a desert wasteland now presses close to the brackish Lake Qarun, meandering tropical rivers once rolled into the sea. Many animals lived in the forests along their banks, and fossil hunters have been finding their remains for more than a half century. When Yale expeditions led by Simons went there in the 1960's to search for fossil primates, they found they often had only to remove the overlying rock, or better yet, sweep away the "desert pavement" — rock cover — and permit the wind to scour out tons of unconsolidated sediments. Fossils sometimes were uncovered.

In one fossil wood zone they discovered a most unusual skull. It looked like the skull of a monkey, though the teeth were much more like a gorilla's. The canines were large and the front premolars enlongated. Simons accurately described the creature as a monkey with the teeth of an ape. He named it *Aegyptopithecus*. In the same area, the wind scoured out several tail bones that seemed assignable to *Aegyptopithecus*, which did not surprise Simons: "Speaking anatomically, it was to be expected that some ancestral

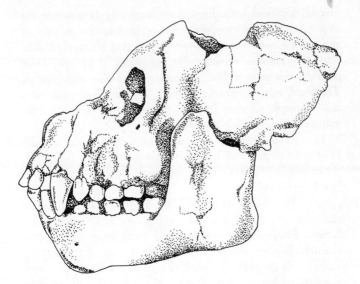

Figure 2.10. *The partially restored skull of* Aegyptopithecus zeuxis, *so named by Elwyn L. Simons, found in the Fayum region of Egypt. The lower jaw is a restoration based on jaw fragments not found in association with the cranium; the incisor teeth of the upper jaw are also restorations. The skull belongs to a species of ape probably ancestral to the dryopithecine apes, and dates back between 26 and 28 million years.*

primate would cross the threshold separating monkey from ape and still bring its tail along."

But the eyes of *Aegyptopithecus* had shifted forward, giving it the better depth perception that would be invaluable in the trees. The creature was big for a tree-dweller, and its feet — some foot bones were found — also suggested adaptation to life in the trees. *Aegyptopithecus* bore the stamp of what was to come.

"The animal was evidently pursuing an arboreal pattern of life directing it along the evolutionary path leading from lemur-like and monkey-like forms to apes and perhaps ultimately to man," said Simons.

A step onward had been taken. For nearly a century

investigators had been digging up teeth and jaw fragments of a fossil primate that also did not fit into the pattern of any known apes. Simons commented that if *Aegyptopithecus* could be called a monkey with the teeth of an ape, these primates might be dubbed apes with the bodies of monkeys. The head was apelike. As a group, the odd assemblage was called dryopithecine — literally, forest ape — but there were many variations within the group.

Some dryopithecines were unearthed in the Siwalik Hills of India and Pakistan, mainly between 1910 and 1937. They generally were represented only by a few teeth and jaw fragments.

In 1948, however, Mary Leakey was scanning a rock face on the Island of Rusinga in Lake Victoria in Kenya. Suddenly her eye caught a speck of gray fossilized enamel. She shouted for her husband who was working nearby, and they eagerly began to dig out her find with dental picks. Behind the exposed tooth the Leakeys saw another tooth, and behind that was something more. In several days of the most painstaking work they dug out a nearly complete skull. It had a rounded forehead like a man. But the canines were long and pointed, and in other ways the skull was that of an ape. The Leakeys named their discovery *Proconsul africanus*, which was later dated at about 24 million years.

"We believe," said Leakey, "that at some stage just about the time of *Proconsul* the stock that ultimately led to man broke away from *Proconsul* himself or from something much like him, and gradually led to you and me. Mary's discovery gave science the first opportunity to see what *Proconsul* had really looked like. Previously we had only jaws and teeth to go on."

Each discoverer of a major fossil or even of a tooth that seems to differ from other teeth tends to set up a special species for its onetime owner and sometimes even a genus. The imposing names given each fossil or its kind have multiplied. Others who have studied the fossils like to "lump" many of them together.

Simons, an authority on the pre-australopithecine fossils, calls both *Proconsul* and the Siwalik finds dryopithecines, but divides them into two series, a larger and a smaller. The larger form, including *Proconsul*, generally has a large snout, protruding incisors, and rather high-crowned teeth. He said: "May it not be that these two sets [*Proconsul* and Siwalik] represent a single species that ranged fairly widely and perhaps over a long period? . . . This species could well be ancestral to the gorilla and chimpanzee." Simons suggested that the second and smaller Indian form might have given rise to the orangutan.

In the early 1960's, about fifteen years after finding *Proconsul*, the Leakeys were working at Fort Ternan, a fossil-rich site in Kenya. When Leakey returned after a short absence, his chief African assistant, Heslon Mukiri, had something special waiting for him. He lifted the lid of a box and Leakey saw a jaw that he knew at once was important. It had what anatomists call a "canine fossa," a depression that occurs in the upper jaw of *Homo* just below the eye socket. It is never seen in the same form among fossil or living apes and monkeys. In man it is an anchor for a muscle controlling the movement of the upper lip, particularly in speech.

The presence of the fossa did not indicate that this creature just unearthed from the past had the ability to speak, but only that the potential for speech was developing. The canine teeth also were small and more like those of a human than an ape. The face was short. Some years later when a lower jaw was discovered in the same area, it was less human in conformation.

At the time of the first find, Leakey named the group represented by the jaw *Kenyapithecus wickeri* (Kenya ape, and *wickeri* for Fred D. P. Wicker, who had financially assisted his work). Evernden and Curtis of the University of California dated *Kenyapithecus* at about 14 million years.

But similar jaws and teeth previously had been found in the fertile Siwalik Hills. They also had similar fossa and the U-shaped dental arch typical of man rather than the V-shaped arch of the apes. The face generally was short, not at all an ape's snout. This peculiar ape had been named *Ramapithecus*.

Simons proposed that *Ramapithecus* and *Kenyapithecus* were much the same kind of creature, and perhaps just progressive dryopithecines. Because the forests of Africa and Asia were continuous at the time, he argued that this was not at all impossible or improbable:

> Separately almost all of these features [of the ramapithecines] can be found among the pongids [apes] but their occurrence in combination in *Ramapithecus brevirostris* is a strong indication of hominid ties.
>
> The transitional nature of these specimens of itself raises the question of the arbitrariness of separating the families Pongidae and Hominidae — a problem which has also been posed recently in connection with another event, the discovery of close biochemical similarities between man and the apes, and in particular the African apes.
>
> Personally I do not see that it very much matters whether members of this genus be regarded as advanced pongids or as primitive hominids.[5]

Advanced apes or primitive humans! The gap or reputed gap between the two was being closed. From ape to man, Simons was proposing, there seemingly was no break, only a gradual becoming, a continuum, a shading from one to the other. It was a transition which might have taken place over millions of years and over a vast part of the earth.

Answers and New Questions

The full story was not told. But much of it was there. The newer studies of anatomy and of the living apes, along with the restudy of the fossils recovered from the earth, all indicated that some early apes slowly and gradually evolved into the part human, part apelike australopithecines that launched the human line. Man was meeting his remoter ancestors: the apes, modified apes, and largely human apes. It had happened. But was it possible? Until the question of how also could be answered or considered, the transition would continue to seem almost impossible and unexplainable.

3

Tools Makyth Man

Millions of monkeys and apes, including the evolving ram-apithecines, ranged through the treetops of the Old and New World forests of 15 million years ago.[1]

   Then the climate changed. The world grew drier, and the lush spreading jungles of earlier times began to shrink. Over a period of about 10 million years, some 5 million square miles were removed from the area that could be occupied by arboreal apes. The domain was being fore-closed as surely as the modern countryside is by the spread of suburbia. Eventually the African and Asian forests became separated. Deserts stretched along the Arabian peninsula where the forests once had joined. Even so, there was plenty of room for the primates and they must have been numerous. If a density of 10 per square mile is assumed, and that is low, there would have been 20,000,000 animals in the transitional population at any one time. Naturally calculations of this kind may be far from the actual facts, but they are introduced to correct the impression that the origin of man occurred necessarily in one restricted small place in one short period of time.

There were millions more of monkeys, for they always outnumbered the apes in the thick green upper world of the forest. For both monkeys and apes the canopy was a relatively safe place to inhabit. A lion or leopard might climb into the heavy lower branches of a thorn tree, but no carnivore could follow a monkey or even the heavier apes out to the ends of the branches. Even a 150-pound ape could safely move far out on a slender limb.

The top of the forest also was a plentiful world. Fruit and tender buds grew on the branches, usually out toward their ends. Food generally was abundant. But as secure and abundant as the arboreal world might have been, it also had its deficiencies. Fruits and buds and insects at times became scarce, perhaps because the more agile monkeys may have beaten the apes to them. And perhaps at times the competition of the apes made life difficult for the monkeys. The bigger apes sometimes drove them away from the best fruit.

But other fruit, insects, and roots could be found on the ground. An ape or monkey that came down from the trees also might be able to reach the ripening bananas in a grove of trees too isolated to reach by leaping from tree to tree. Lions, hyenas, and other carnivores were a greater menace on the ground, but if trees were nearby, an animal on the forest floor could quickly escape by climbing. The ground offered many advantages, despite its dangers.

For some or possibly all of these reasons, and perhaps for other reasons now unknown, some monkeys and apes came to the ground.

An unknown number of monkeys did come down to the ground. Most, though, could not survive there; they perished and their species became extinct. Some of their fossilized bones have been found. Only three groups — the Patas, the baboons, and the geladas — succeeded as ground-dwellers, and a few others as partial inhabitants of the ground.

Though many opportunities opened, all three remained quadrupeds. They scampered over the forest floor and through the underbrush exactly as they had through the trees, on all fours. With hands and feet involved in locomotion, the hands were never free to use objects of any kind in defense. All found other ways of fighting off the dangers and enemies of the ground.

The Patas monkey developed a decoy system and speed to outwit and outdistance a predator. If a hungry carnivore approached, the dominant male Patas would run away screeching and jumping about in the grass until the marauder could not fail to see him and be drawn into pursuit. With his great speed Patas then could usually elude even the fast leopard. All the while the females and the young "froze" in the tall grass, successfully playing dead. This adaptation to life on the ground worked well; the Patas monkey survives and flourishes into the present.

The other two monkeys that came down from the trees, the baboon and the geladas, found safety in fighting with the face. The males became big enough and fierce enough with their slashing canine teeth to stand off and vanquish even the largest carnivores. The male baboons also sometimes fought as a group. Irven De Vore of Harvard University watched a group of baboons and impala feeding together, as they often did, in a grassy area near a grove of trees. He saw three cheetahs approaching. Both the impalas and baboons stirred warily and uneasily, but neither fled, though the impalas were a favorite quarry of the cheetah. As the cheetahs drew close, a large male baboon stepped forward, baring his knife-sharp fangs and defying the marauders. The cheetahs fled. Not only were the baboons protected, but the impalas also found safety. Evidently the impalas had learned from experience to rely on the baboons for protection.

Figure 3.1. *Primates live in groups which, in turn, live close to many other kinds of animals. Both social life and ecology are fundamental in primate evolution. Photographed in the Amboseli Reserve, Kenya, are: a baboon troop (above); zebras, impalas, and baboons (opposite page).*

The Old World monkeys' coming to the ground showed only minor problems in adaptation for many of the forms. For the vast majority of monkeys, ground living takes place close to the trees — and this is true even for most baboons. For Old World monkeys the problem was not so much that of ground living, as of the anatomical and behavioral adaptations necessitated by living away from trees.

But the Old World monkey that descended from the trees went no further in adaptations to life on the ground. Only one step was taken. No more.

In the New World not a single species of monkey came down from the trees and survived on the ground. Here not even the primary step was taken. One of several reasons may have been that the New World monkeys are small and no very small primates have adapted to life on the ground.

Another part of the problem could be investigated in the modern laboratory. At the University of California at Berkeley, Old World and New World monkeys were placed in the same cage and closely observed as they moved over the same area and obstacles. As the scientists carefully watched, they saw that the New World monkeys were less efficient than the Old in moving over the ground. Examination revealed the reason.

The lumbar region of the back of the New World monkeys is curved differently, and it is used less when the monkey moves, and particularly when it jumps. The curvature appears to be related to the monkey's prehensile tail, which generally had been considered a locomotor adaptation, but in laboratory study turned out to be a feeding adaptation. The monkeys use their tails, not to move faster or more surely, but to hold a branch and steady themselves while they feed with both hands. If the tail structures of American monkeys impede movement on the ground, or do not facilitate it, their tails may have precluded their successfully moving to the ground. The laboratory studies suggested that this clumsiness on the ground may have been a factor in their staying in the trees.

It had traditionally been thought that some primates were forced to come to the ground when the slow shrinkage of the forests began. But this desiccation (drying) — some 5 to 10 million years ago — occurred in the New World as well as in the Old. Instead of forcing the monkeys to adapt to a new way of life, it led to the extinction of many species. If the New World monkeys were forced down and out of the trees, they perished instead of learning to live on the ground.

But much more information is needed before this interpretation can be considered more than a suggestion. The situation in the New World implies that the effects of the reduction of forests on the behavior of the primates will depend on the precise nature of their arboreal adaptation. If primates are small and adapted to certain kinds of arboreal feeding, the probable result is extinction, not ground adaptation as the desiccation theory suggests.

The prospects were narrowing. None of the New World monkeys succeeded on the ground, and the three Old World species that abandoned the arboreal for the

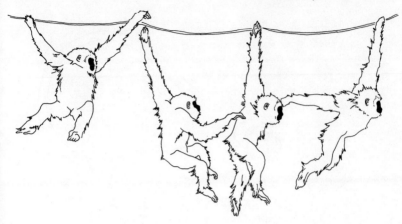

Figure 3.2. *These drawings show the movements of a gibbon brachiating.*

terrestrial life stopped with this transition. To this day they have continued as quadrupeds.

The story, though, does not end in the trees or with quadrupedal primates living on the land or partly on the land. The apes also were venturing down.

In Asia the orangutan and the gibbon occasionally climbed down from the treetops. But these large apes did not often come down or remain for long, and they evolved no structural adaptations for locomotion on the ground. Their basic structure continues to be for living in trees. The gibbon swings and hurtles from branch to branch with a grace that the English naturalist William Charles Martin described as "aerial." So light and free are its movements, it scarcely seems to touch the branches in its agile progress. It rarely leaves the tops of trees. The orangutan, on the other hand, is a slow and cautious mover, but is little more drawn to the ground.

Thus two others that might have come to the ground turned back, or did not adapt to the harsh land below their treetops. The prospects that any ape would learn to live on the ground were further narrowed.

But in Africa one group of apes took a different

Figure 3.3. *This drawing contrasts with Figure 3.2, as it shows the locomotion of a quadrupedal monkey (a vervet).*

course, a course that ultimately would lead to man. This group of apes, perhaps one of the ramapithecines, found life on the forest floor not only possible but rewarding. Only a few scant fossils tell of this stage in evolution. However, studies of anatomy, biochemistry, and living animals are helping to fill in this long and crucial period in history.

The apes climbing down from the tree were relatively large. Why largeness should have been an advantage was not clear, but it is a matter of record that the smaller forms perished or retreated to the safer treetops.

The apes coming down for the food the land held out had short, wide, and shallow trunks as compared to the elongated trunks of the monkeys. They also had shoulders quite unlike those of the monkeys. The ape shoulder permits a strong, powerful reach, particularly to the side. If a branch is not overly large or stable, and an ape wants to reach a nearby limb, he can grab the first with his hands and swing across to a new handhold on the other. The method of swinging the dangling body to a new position is called "brachiation." A monkey, in contrast, crosses the same branch on all fours.

If a branch is sturdy enough, however, the ape also might resort to all fours, or by standing largely upright and balancing with a hold on some upper branch, might even take a few steps on two legs.

The long, mobile arms of the apes with their powerful flexor muscles also make it easy for them to climb and eat by reaching. The apes often hang from a branch by one arm and feed with the other. Or they hold a branch with one hand and stretch the other hand as far out as possible to reach a ripe fig. A human does exactly the same thing when he wants to pick up something just out of easy reach.

There is a profound similarity in the motions of the arms of man and apes, and on any playground one can see humans brachiating from bars, hanging by one hand, and exhibiting a variety of motions and postures which are similar to those of the apes. Man still is a brachiator. He is simply the one who is least frequently in the situation which calls forth this behavior. Our legs are too heavy and our arms too weak for efficient brachiation, but when we climb we climb like apes, not like monkeys.

Along with this unusual structure of the trunk and arms, came changes in the lower back. No backbones of these early apes have been discovered, but in some New World monkeys that also evolved brachiation, the structural mechanisms of the back were similarly reduced.

When these New World monkeys are studied in more detail, they should provide a much fuller understanding of the nature of brachiation, and aid in the reconstruction of the locomotor patterns of the formative apes. These forms may have been in a behavioral stage very similar to that of *Ateles* (the New World monkey with the altered back).

Again the structure of a living primate provides an insight into the special structure the apes of 10 million or more years ago evolved when they left the trees. The apes backing down from trees — their method of descending — could stand on their hind legs and even take a few steps upright. It was a useful ability. Observers of living animals see them frequently standing to look over high grass and survey the scene for friends, enemies, or food. But they cannot go far on two legs. They are inefficient bipedalists.

If it had not been for a modified method of locomotion they might have gone no further. But these apes coming to the ground either had or were developing another method of walking across the forest floor — they knuckle-walked! Instead of placing the hand flat on the ground as monkeys do, they curled under the fingers of the hands, and used the knuckles as a compromise forefoot and hand. This method of walking was the key to eventual upright walking, to human evolution, and to man.

By knuckle-walking, an ape on the ground could move from one isolated group of trees to another. If danger threatened he still could climb to safety. The knuckle gait did not interfere with the structures that enabled him to climb or move around in the trees.

Although apes in zoos always had been seen standing half erect with their weight resting on the knuckles of either one or both hands, the posture was dismissed as one more peculiarity of the caged animal. The knuckle stance seemed unimportant; it was assumed that in the wilds the chimpanzee and gorilla spent most of their lives in the trees and that they moved through the trees by swinging or brachiating from branch to branch and from tree to tree. When the anatomy of the arm was studied it was treated as though nearly all its use lay in hanging.

The new field studies suddenly upset this neat theory. Schaller reported that gorillas are primarily ground-living animals. Nearly all their time is spent knuckle-walking on the forest floor, foraging along for the wild celery, the buds, and the insects they eat. Only occasionally they climb into the trees to sun on a branch or to make a nest for an afternoon nap.

Jane van Lawick-Goodall found that the chimpanzees were also largely ground-dwellers. Like the gorillas, the chimps walked through the forest on their knuckles. Only on a few occasions did they walk upright. Far from being incidental, knuckle-walking was the primary means of locomotion for both the great apes.

Russell H. Tuttle, professor of anatomy and anthropology at the University of Chicago, made a five-year study of the primate hands. He reported that knuckle-walking gave speed and steadiness to the gait of the chimpanzees and gorillas.

Knuckle-walking made the transition from ape to man far easier to understand. If the apes shifting to a life on the ground had tried to walk on two feet they would have been so awkward and slow they would easily have been run down and devoured by the carnivores. Man, with bipedalism developed in full, still is easily outrun by a lion or a cheetah. Clumsy bipeds also would have had small chance of catching the small game that they hunt when they have the opportunity or even the young that are their ordinary prey.

It was always difficult to explain how a creature less fleet than man could have survived at all. A knuckle-walking stage gets around the problem, as shown by the contemporary chimpanzee.

The chimpanzee can move very rapidly quadrupedally and then climb out of danger if necessary. The chimpanzee knuckle-walks, climbs for feeding and escape, brachiates, and may walk bipedally for moderate distances, especially when carrying something.

If changed selection pressures (on the ground) favored the bipedal part of the behavior repertoire, then the beginnings of the human kind of bipedal walking and running might evolve while the animal could still move rapidly as a knuckle-walker and escape danger by climbing.

Knuckle-walking got the new ground-dwellers around the possibly fatal dangers of being a slow, inefficient bipedalist, as most monkeys are. It also helped to solve the anatomical problem of walking on two legs instead of four. To walk on two legs in the human way, the hind legs must first combine the functions of both the forelegs and the hind legs in the quadrupedal gait.

Careful studies of the gorilla disclosed that when the huge animals knuckle-walk or occasionally walk on two legs, the heel hits the ground first. This is an essential characteristic of human walking. It is not the way monkeys walk. The monkey, and the human child learning to take its first steps, put the foot down toe first. It is a most uncertain and wobbly gait. Until the human youngster learns to use the heel, he totters and soon sits down with a little thump. When the heel strikes the ground first, the foot does not bend, and there is power for the next step.

The gorilla foot looks like a monkey foot with the toe out at the side. But it works like a human foot. Structurally all that needs to be done with the ape foot to turn it into a human foot is to bring the big toe in line with the other toes and reduce the length of the toes.

Traditional morphologists looking at the gorilla or chimpanzee foot saw it like a monkey's foot. They were not considering stability or the functional problem of the mid-foot area, but said, "Well, this is like a monkey's foot because the toe is off to the side." This misses the point that it is extraordinarily like a human foot. The more an ape's foot is studied the more it seems like a human foot.

Long arms also are essential for knuckle-walking. The apes moving out on the forest floor must have had them, for their descendants have them today. The anthropomorphous, or humanlike, apes are long-armed, and many humans have arms with the same range of length.

On the ground, even part-time, apes found life very different. An ape whose hands were not totally involved in locomotion was freer to use them in other ways, which soon proved to be a great advantage. If all food did not have to be consumed on the spot where it was found and some could be carried away, the carrier might be better fed.

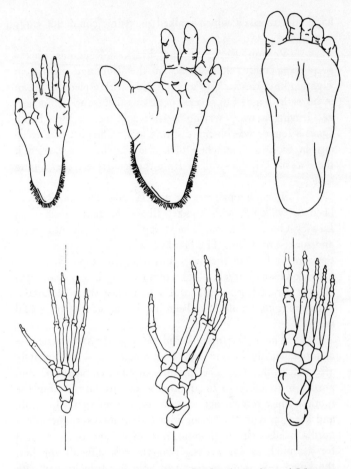

Figure 3.4. *The external structure (top) of the feet of* Macaca, *chimpanzee, and* Homo sapiens *(left to right) contrasted with their skeletal structure. The lines above and below the foot skeletons show the functional axis, which comes at the same point in the chimpanzee and in man.*

And the knuckle-walkers could carry. The fingers could curl around a small branch or a piece of fruit and hold it firmly while an ape moved smartly along on his knuckles. There was little interference with his gait. On the other

73

hand, the monkey which walked on palms could not carry food.

Vernon Reynolds and Frances Reynolds photographed a male chimpanzee in the Budongo Forest in Uganda knuckle-walking along a road with a piece of rattan in his right hand. On several occasions they saw a chimpanzee leaving a tree carrying a fruited branch in one hand. Once a female was observed sitting in a mahogany tree feeding on fruits still attached to a branch. She had carried it there as she knuckle-walked from the fruit tree to her dining spot.

The chimpanzees of the Gombe Stream Reserve liked to walk off with blankets from the tents in the van Lawick-Goodalls' camp. They happily tore them into pieces and sucked on them. The blankets were either tucked under the arm or held in the hand and dragged along. Jane van Lawick-Goodall tracked one chimp as he dragged a stolen blanket for at least a mile and a half up a steep mountain. Such dragging would have been impossible for a quadrupedal animal.

The ability to walk and carry at the same time also counted heavily in one way that directly and immediately affected evolution. The infants of the chimpanzee and gorilla must cling to the mother's hair to survive, for the mother must remain active, moving around to feed, climb, and keep up with the troop. Sometimes, however, the infant gorilla needs help in clinging, and may have to be assisted for as much as six weeks. Though it is difficult for her, the knuckle-walking mother can hold her baby to her with one hand and walk on her other's knuckles and two legs. An observer reported that a baboon mother fell behind most of a band. Every few steps she had to stop to rest. If an adult male had not stayed beside her, stopping when she stopped and walking when she walked, she and the infant she was supporting might well have been taken by a predator. An ape lagging behind the troop is in constant danger.

An ape able to stand up on two legs and to use his freed hands for flailing about and throwing also is more

Figure 3.5. *This photograph shows Faben brandishing a stick upon seeing his reflection in a mirror.*

likely to win a fight, and winning can influence both survival and the production of offspring. The most effective fighter has an evolutionary advantage.

Jane van Lawick-Goodall on three different occasions observed a male chimpanzee threatening a baboon. The chimp, rearing up on his hind legs and swinging his arms around above his head, ran toward the baboon. The baboon fled. She also observed Goliath, in a fit of rage when David Graybeard got more bananas, seize a stick and wave it in the air, and then drag it behind him as he ran back and forth. Another time, when the belligerent Goliath was charging a native, he picked up an axe and swung it over his head before dropping it.

When a storm was breaking or in other times of excitement, Jane van Lawick-Goodall often saw the large male chimpanzees break branches off the trees and run bipedally down a hill while they waved and thrashed about with their "weapons." They would reach the bottom, return to the top, and repeat the startling, noisy performance.

All the observers saw the great apes throw branches and sometimes stones. Sometimes they fired them overhand and sometimes underhand — an ability that they share with humans and no other animal. The weapons were never precisely aimed and they seldom hit, but they frequently scared away the enemy or an unwelcome bystander.

The difference between an ape's throwing and a small boy's is that the ape in the wild does not aim accurately. Neither does he collect a pile of fist-sized stones and practice throwing them at a tree until he can hit it or some similar target. In a zoo though, an ape often develops remarkable skill in throwing objects at anyone he dislikes.

Because modern apes use sticks and stones, the scientists believe that the early apes taking up life on the ground similarly brandished weapons.

K. R. L. Hall, in a review of such behaviors,[2] proposed that the use of weapons evolved in two possible ways: (1) either as a consequence of the use of larger sticks for utilitarian purposes; or (2) from the repeated discovery that a stick waved in display may do damage if it actually hits the animal against whom the display is directed and that a rock thrown in the direction of another animal during a display occasionally may hit and vanquish it. As Hall indicated, the apes did not use objects in anger alone.

"Both gorilla and chimpanzee show a strong tendency to manipulate as well as throw objects," said Jane B. Lancaster in her paper "On the Evolution of Tool Using Behavior."[3] "Goodall has collected more than 1,000 of the twigs and grass blades — the tools — chimpanzees use in fishing for termites. Some will search carefully for just the right piece and then spend time preparing it. A few prepare a little pile of stems before starting to termite, and some make the twigs even before the nest is found."

Along with the use of leaves for grooming, of leaf sponges for sopping up water, and of sticks for prying out roots or other foods, the great apes far surpass any other animal except man in tool-use.

"The chimpanzee does more kinds of things with objects than all the other mammals together," said Lancaster.

Many other animals use "tools" in special ways. The finch, for example, may use a cactus spine to extract grubs. But such use represents a behavioral pattern to aid in feeding. No special brain or hand structures have developed to make tool-use possible.

To add to the difference, chimpanzees and gorillas learn their skills through watching other apes perform. A young chimp will sit for many minutes watching its mother termite, and when she quits may pick up her fishing stalk and awkwardly try fishing for himself. As Lancaster said,

> The tool using behavior of chimpanzees suggests the kind of ape ancestor that might be postulated for the origin of the hominid line. It would be an ape that used tools for many different reasons and in many different ways, no matter how insignificant the tool, like leaf sponges, or how undramatic, like termiting twigs, or how inefficient, like a clumsily swung stick.
>
> The more kinds of tools the ape uses the more likely he is to be an ancestor, because it would have been the

accumulated influence of many reasons for using tools that would have taken selective pressure off the specific situation, the specific tool, and the specific movement.

Selective pressure was put on a hand that could use many tools skillfully and on a brain capable of learning these skills. Natural selection would then have acted on a broader category of behavior, one involving the brain, the hand, many objects, and a wide variety of social and ecological situations.[4]

The new findings on chimpanzee tool-use made possible daring and formerly impossible speculation about the evolution of ape into apeman and man. They suggested that the common ancestors of the great apes and man were beginning tool-users. Only a few years earlier when simply chipped stone tools were found in Africa and some turned up in deposits that held the fossilized bones of the australopithecines or apemen, it was fiercely denied that these small-brained beings could have made them. The theory that such creatures could have performed so human a skill was ridiculed. Additional finds and study were to settle the dispute during the last two decades. The australopithecines were the toolmakers. Then the great apes were identified as at least casual toolmakers and users. Though the fossil proof still is lacking, it is strongly indicated that the apes after their descent from the trees became toolmakers and users of at least a primitive kind. The evolutionary gap was being closed and the toolmaking that is one mark of human intelligence was carried back some 3 million to 4 million years, a time that would have been inconceivable only a decade or two ago.

A perspective on the problem of learning to use objects may be given in the following way: Primate hands evolved from claw-bearing paws early in the Eocene. For 50 million years in many families of primates, dozens of genera and hundreds of species, hands were used for feeding, grooming, and locomotion, but in all of this time and in all of these manipulative creatures, substantial use of objects as an adaptive mechanism evolved only once.

Negative evidence suggests that a very special set of circumstances is needed to account for the beginning of tool-using and that digital dexterity, although necessary, is a very small part of the explanation. The special situation is knuckle-walking.

These knuckle-walking primates had come a long way. Some 8 million to 10 million years ago, one group living in the deepest forest dropped out of the slow progression. As time went on it specialized into the modern gorilla.

The other primates continued on what man considers the more progressive course. More years went by. Then another group stayed behind or branched off. This was the chimpanzee. These bright animals are well adapted to the stable world in which they live. Food is plentiful and enemies few in their forests. There was little selective pressure for change in a largely unchanging environment, so they flourished until recently. Only in the twentieth century did they encounter difficulty, when their greatly changed relative, man, began to preempt more of their forests for himself and his cattle. Except in a few preserves, the chimpanzee now does not have a very good chance of surviving into the future.

While the gorilla and chimpanzee were beginning to go their own way, some other primates began wandering out of the deep forest and toward the forest edges that Simons calls the "woodland," and then on to the savannah or the more open country just beyond. Here was more space, with fewer trees, less underbrush, different foods, and different animals. Under these new circumstances, selection favored the most bipedal of the apes and those best able to fight off the speedier animals of this drier land.

As the locomotor pattern evolved in response to the new pressures, more effective tool-use also evolved. Locomotion and tool-use affected each other in a feedback relationship and each is at once cause and effect of the other. The use of tools was not made possible by a preceding bipedal adaptation, nor was tool-use a simple discovery. Probably it was the selective result of repetitive events in thousands of populations of apes over millions of years.

Tools and Weapons

As large populations of apes became more surely bipedal and as the hands were increasingly freed from locomotion, attacks with weapons must have slowly replaced attacks with the face and the teeth. The weapons proved a superior way of fighting.

About a century ago Charles Darwin argued that the large teeth of the adult male ape ancestor were replaced by tools.

"The early male forefathers of man were probably furnished with great canine teeth," Darwin wrote in *The Descent of Man*, "but as they gradually acquired the habit of using stones, clubs, and other weapons for fighting with their enemies or rivals they would use their jaws and teeth less and less. In this case the jaws, together with the teeth, would become reduced in size."

Darwin again was right. The fossil teeth that have been found show this evolution. The smaller teeth and the smaller jaw and neck structures that went with them are evidence that the apes beginning to live on the forest edges used weapons they could manipulate with their hands. If the canines had been reduced before their owners learned to fight with sticks and stones, such apes in all probability would not have survived to hand down their smaller teeth to their descendants. They would have been quite defenseless.

Furthermore, a primate wandering away from the trees in pursuit of some quarry had to be ready at any moment to fight. He could not start searching for a stick or stone when he caught up with his game. His weapon had to be in hand and it had to be used skillfully.

The skills had to be learned, and they could only be learned sufficiently in the earliest years, starting with play. And if there was to be enough time for childhood play, the pre-australopithecines and australopithecines had to mature more slowly than their ape ancestors. A Simons and Pilbeam study of the teeth of the ramapithecines has indicated that they matured more slowly than the apes.[5] Living out in the savannah away from the trees would have come long after ground living, knuckle-walking, toolmaking, and tool-using, and slower maturation.

The creatures venturing out from the edges of the forest departed in other ways from their ancestral apes. They were small — in comparison to humans — probably between four and five feet tall. Nor were they heavy — the 500-pound gorilla had remained behind. They also were relatively slow; they had no ruses like those of the Patas monkey and lacked the fighting canines of their ancestors.

To survive in the more open, drier lands they had to replace escape, size, speed, deception, and built-in weapons with other strengths and defenses. This they did successfully, as history proves. The move to the forest edges, dangerous as it was, was another beginning, not an end. They were ready with their two-legged gait, their tool-use, their prolonged time for learning. They also had the anatomical and social adaptation to go further.

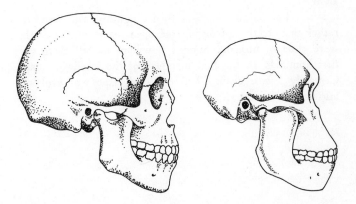

Figure 3.6. *These drawings of skulls show the relatively little difference between the canines of* Homo sapiens (left) *and those of* Australopithecus africanus. *See Figure 4.4, page 99, which shows the difference between the teeth of* Australopithecus *and a* gorilla.

However, this unique transition took time, a prodigious amount of time. It was only accomplished in about 10 million years, probably in the span from 15 million years ago to 5 million years.

If we assume a generation time of about ten years, then 800,000 generations separate populations of the forms moving out to the savannah from populations of late Miocene apes. The estimated 10 million years and the 800,000 generations had produced changes that had seemed impossible.

"If the gorilla and a few allied forms had become extinct," Darwin said, "it might have been argued with great force and apparent truth that an animal could not have been gradually converted from a quadruped to a biped, as all individuals in an intermediate condition would have been miserably ill-fitted for progression."

Darwin did not have the field studies, the fossil discoveries, and the biochemical data to inform him, though he argued correctly from what he did know. It remained for the newer studies to show how and why such a nearly impossible transition was made by one group and one group alone.

The partially upright forms, fighting with weapons rather than teeth and daring the open spaces of the earth, were close to humans. Simons is willing to call them the first hominids, or the first members of the family of man. Certainly a vast change had occurred. Ape was evolving into primitive man.

4

Missing Links

Dr. Raymond A. Dart was dressing for a wedding which was to be held in his Johannesburg home when a delivery service arrived with two large wooden boxes. The doctor, a professor of anatomy at the University of Witwatersrand, knew that the crates contained fossils from a lime quarry at Taung in the Bechuanaland Protectorate. The time could not have been worse, but he pulled off his wing collar, and over the protests of his wife rushed out to see what the boxes might hold. He pried off the lid of the first, and could make out traces of fossilized eggs and turtle shells. This was not too promising. The doctor was hoping for a fossil baboon skull, similar to one previously found at the limeworks. Dart went on to the second box, quite oblivious

85

to the warnings of his wife that the guests would be arriving at any moment. As he pulled off the lid he saw a cast or mold of the interior of a skull.

"I knew at a glance that this was no ordinary anthropoidal [great ape] brain. Here was the replica of a brain three times as large as that of a baboon, and considerably bigger than that of any adult chimpanzee. . . . But it was not big enough for primitive man."

Was there a face to go with the brain? Dart feverishly ransacked through the rocks. He found a large stone with a depression into which the cast fitted perfectly. Faintly visible in it was the outline of part of a skull and a lower jaw. The face might well be somewhere in the block.

Excited and absorbed, the doctor was standing there in the front driveway of his home when the bridegroom arrived. He was Dart's close friend and the doctor was to serve as the best man in the wedding. The bride was on the way. At this point the doctor had to tear himself away from the boxes, but he carried the little cast into the house with him.

The moment the last guest departed, Dart was back at his boxes and the puzzling skull. In fact every possible minute during the next seventy-three days was spent trying to free the skull from its matrix. The doctor had no experience in such exacting work and no special equipment for it, but he went at it with the greatest of care, and his best tool proved to be one of his wife's knitting needles. On the seventy-third day the stone parted. What emerged was a child's face, a youngster with a full set of milk teeth. The first permanent molars were just beginning to erupt.

Was this child ape or human? If it were an ape, the doctor argued to himself, what was an anthropoid with a brain larger than that of a chimpanzee and as large as a gorilla's doing in South Africa, more than 2,000 miles from the jungles in which the great apes lived? Dart knew that there had been little climatic change in South Africa in the last few million years. The dry, treeless veldt of the

Transvaal would have offered none of the foods on which the great apes normally feed.

Besides the little skull was shaped like that of a human. Though the skull was low, it had a true forehead and none of the ape's heavy eyebrow ridges. The canines were small, too — not the tusks of an ape. As he studied the position the skull must have occupied on the body, the doctor's conviction grew. This creature emerging from the block of stone had walked upright.

It was, by all the signs a manlike ape, rather than

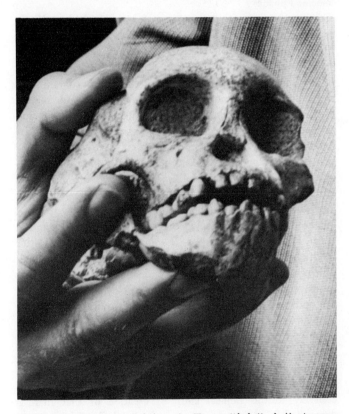

Figure 4.1. *The hand holding the Taung "baby" skull gives an indication of its size.*

the apelike man of fiction. It might be — Dart thought that it was — the creature the world had been imagining since Darwin's day and calling the "missing link."

But Dart was cautious. He named his "baby" *Australopithecus africanus* (*Austral* for south, *pithecus* for ape). He took the "correct" step of preparing a preliminary report for *Nature*, the English scientific journal. But in his article he said openly, "The specimen is of importance because it exhibits an extinct race of apes intermediate between living anthropoids and man." It appeared in the issue of February 7, 1925.

Once again there was a furor. Sir Arthur Keith, the leading authority on fossil man and Conservator of the Huntarian Museum in the Royal College of Surgeons, conceded that Dart's "baby" was a "remarkable" ape but held that it should be placed in the same group or subfamily as the chimpanzees and gorillas. Sir Arthur added that it seemed to be "near akin to both." Other anthropologists expressed doubt or carped about the "barbarous" name Dart had chosen.

Popular interest ran high. Newspapers and magazines widely reported the "finding of the missing link," and the *Spectator* ran a contest for the best epitaph in verse or prose. The classic music hall joke was given a new twist — "Who was the girl I saw you with last night — was she from Taung?" The Sunday *London Times* printed a letter from a "plain but sane woman" asking Professor Dart, "How can you, with such a wonderful gift of God-given genius become a traitor to your Creator by making yourself the active agent of Satan and his ready tool?"

The press also carried a story from the United States: "Professor Dart's theory that the Taung skull is a missing link has evidently not convinced the legislature of Tennessee. The governor of the state has signed an anti-evolution bill which forbids the teaching of any theory contrary to the Biblical story of creation or that man is descended from any lower orders of animals."

Among the relatively few messages of congratulations was one from Dr. Robert Broom, a Scottish-born physician who had been drawn to South Africa in his search for fossil mammals. Broom was seeking the answer to another debated question of the day: Did the mammals arise from an amphibious or a reptilian ancestor?

Six weeks later the doors of Dart's laboratory burst open and the redoubtable Dr. Broom strode in. He went straight to the bench on which he saw the skull and dropped to his knees for a closer look and what he later said was "adoration of our ancestor." He remained over the weekend for an intensive study and was completely convinced. In an article that he promptly wrote for *Nature* he said: "In *Australopithecus* we have a being with a chimpanzee-like jaw, but a sub-human brain. We seem justified in concluding that in this new form discovered by Professor Dart we have a connecting link between the higher apes and one of the lowest human types."[1]

After the initial flurry the world's interest in the outlandish Taung "baby" faded rapidly. The anthropology headlines were being made by the search for man's earliest ancestors in Outer Mongolia and in the caves at Choukoutien near Peking. It was confidently anticipated that Asia would prove to be the cradle of mankind. Dart summed up the attitude: "What dissonant squawkings were these from the puny South African infant at Taung? What was the use of a baby anthropoid when you were looking for men — primitive men at that?"[2]

Dart and Broom realized that only the discovery of an adult *Australopithecus* would overcome the world's condescending doubts and joking unacceptance. Broom said that Dart felt hurt and discredited by the reception of his discovery. Dart himself emphasized that as dean of the Faculty of Medicine he had neither the time nor the inclination to continue the search for the necessary adult form. He was too busy, he said, to sit brooding about what had happened.

Neither Dart nor Broom gave up their intense interest in the little skull itself. During the next four years they worked painstakingly to free the skull completely from its matrix, and finally in 1929 succeeded in separating the upper and lower jaws. This made it possible for the first time to see the full pattern of the teeth. When Dart sent casts to the world's authorities, Dr. W. K. Gregory, curator of comparative anatomy of the American Museum of Natural History, was convinced: "In the light of all this additional evidence if *Australopithecus* is not literally a missing link between our older dryopithecoid group and primitive man, what conceivable combination of ape and human characters would ever be admitted as such?"[3]

The details of the teeth often provide strong evidence for proving relationships. The teeth of the Taung "baby" are similar to man's and very different from the apes'.

Broom, unlike Dart, was eager to take up the search for more material. However, he was tied to his medical practice in the little town of Maquassi, inconveniently far from both Taung or any other likely apeman sites. Field Marshal Smuts, the scholarly premier of the Union of South Africa, decided to do something about this unfortunate situation, and appointed Broom curator of vertebrate paleontology in the Transvaal Museum in Pretoria.

"Gen. Smuts thought it a pity that I should be spending my latter years in medical work when I might be devoting all my time to scientific work," Broom said.[4]

The doctor was then sixty-eight, and in 1936 when he was ready to start the field search he was nearing seventy. Broom soon unearthed some unknown species of rats and moles and an ancient baboon skull.

Some students of Dart's told Broom about some baboon skulls they had found in another limestone quarry at Sterkfontein. Broom quickly arranged a trip to the site. The town, about thirty miles from Johannesburg, had grown up during the gold rush of 1886, and in the intervening years millions in gold had been taken out, as well as a wide array of fossils. Boys were always picking up the fossilized bones of extinct baboons and other animals. The town had even published a guidebook urging visitors to "Come to Sterkfontein and find the missing link."

Dr. Broom and the students arrived on August 9, 1936, and went first to the limeworks quarry. The manager, G. W. Barlow, knew about the Taung skull and agreed at once to keep an eye out for any other fossilized bones his quarrying might blast out. He "rather thought" he had seen some skulls of the kind the doctor described. Usually he sold any "nice bones and skulls" to Sunday visitors to the quarry.

When the doctor returned the next week, Barlow asked, "Is this what you're after?" and handed him about two-thirds of a "beautiful fossil brain cast." Broom recognized instantly that it was the cast of an adult australopithecine skull. It had been blasted out only that morning. The doctor rushed over to the pile of debris that had been left and began digging through it in search for the skull that had made the impress. By nightfall he still was empty-handed. The next day, however, after three hours of digging and sorting through the dusty pile the doctor found the base of the skull, the upper jaw, and fragments of the cranium. When all the bits and pieces were cleaned and assembled he had a nearly complete skull of an adult with nearly all of the half-man, half-ape characteristics that the world had considered a freak or an impossibility in the Taung baby.

"To have started out to look for an adult skull of *Australopithecus* and to have found an adult of at least an allied form in about three months was a record of which we felt there was no reason to be ashamed," Broom said. "To have gone to Sterkfontein and found what we wanted within nine days was even better."

The doctor continued to visit his fossil "gold mine" at regular intervals. All the workers were alerted to watch for any fossils and always had a stack awaiting his inspection — bits of skull, teeth, and quantities of animal fossils. "Every trip cost me some shillings in tips, but it was worth it," Broom remarked.

One fine morning in June, 1938, when Broom arrived, Barlow met him with an air of promise. "I have something nice for you this morning," he said, handing the doctor a palate of a large apeman. The manager had obtained it from a schoolboy, Gert Terblanche, who lived on a farm at Kromdraai about two miles away.

The doctor jumped in his car and rattled off to the Terblanche farm. Gert was at school, but Broom succeeded in getting him out of his classes by agreeing to deliver a little talk to the students on the fossils in their area. Gert led the doctor to a cache where he had secreted his finds and presented him with a "fine jaw with some beautiful teeth." During the next few days the doctor and the boy recovered many additional scraps of bone from the place where Gert had dug out the jaw. When they were all fitted together the doctor had most of the left side of a skull, as well as the lower right jaw.

The new skull was surprising and puzzling. It showed a mixture of apelike and manlike characteristics, but it differed notably from *Australopithecus*. The jaw was more massive, the grinding teeth larger, and the face flatter and more apelike. In their form, however, the teeth were distinctly human. Dr. Broom was convinced that the being he and Gert had screened from the rock of a former cave was so different from the Taung baby, or *A. africanus*,

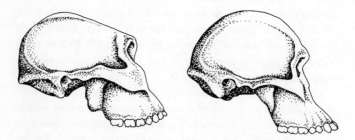

Figure 4.2. *A comparison of the skulls of* Australopithecus robustus (*left*) *and* A. africanus.

that it would have to be assigned to a genus of its own. He named it *Paranthropus robustus* (robust near man).

The claim that not one, but two genera had existed in one small area of South Africa further increased the disbelief of the English authorities. "Of course the critics did not know the whole of the facts," said Dr. Broom. "When one has jealous opponents one does not let them know everything."[5]

The doctor had not revealed that the sites, which lay within easy sight of each other across a fairly narrow valley, had been occupied at different times. When *P. robustus* lived, the local climate had been wet and the vegetation heavy. In the time of *Australopithecus* at Sterkfontein and Taung, the climate had been the semidesert that it had remained through the rest of history. Even the extinct animals differed at the two sites. Many fossil horses were found at Kromdraai, but none were found at Sterkfontein. At Kromdraai the excavators had dug out many fossilized bones of the giant dassie or hyrax, as it is called in the Bible; at Sterkfontein only a small form was found. The jackals, baboons, and saber-toothed tigers at Kromdraai also were distinctive.

At the time Broom had no accurate way of dating the fossils he was unearthing or the geological formations in which they lay. At Sterkfontein the caves in which the apemen had lived had filled gradually with stalactites and stalagmites and with dense layers of water-deposited travertine. The forming stone surrounded and covered the bones that lay in the caves. In time the caves filled in, often the roofs collapsed. The modern quarrying operations exposed the filled-in former caves.

At Kromdraai, erosion of the surrounding earth had left the hard consolidated cave deposits as small kopjes or mounds. The masses of bones in the former caves were compacted into a conglomerate called "bone breccia." But at neither site was there any clear stratification to give a clue to time. Only general estimates of the age of the caves and their contents could be made.

The outbreak of World War II forced Broom to stop his work in the field. By that time he had accumulated much material, though in the rush of collecting it he had not had time to prepare and study it thoroughly. The war years gave him that opportunity, and in 1946 Broom and G. W. H. Schepers were able to publish a full report, *The South African Fossil Ape-Man*.

The opposition began to crumble. The South African discoveries could no longer be brushed aside. Sir Wilfrid E. Le Gros Clark, who had been a skeptic, was so impressed with the data presented in the Broom book that he arranged to visit South Africa in 1947. Before he went, he carefully examined the skulls and teeth of more than a hundred modern anthropoid apes to determine the normal variations in their anatomical structure so he could compare these measurements with those of the australopithecines. The South Africans gladly opened their collections to him.

"The results of my studies were illuminating, not only because they made me realize how much more profitable it is to study original specimens than to rely on casts or photographs, but because they convinced me that Dart and Broom were essentially right in their assessment of the significance of the Australopithecines as the probable precursors of more advanced types of the Hominidae," Sir Wilfrid said publicly, at the First Pan African Congress on Prehistory held shortly afterward at Nairobi.

He had a battle on his hands. Professor Wood Jones, a distinguished anatomist, argued that man had evolved, independently of monkeys and anthropoid apes, from the tarsiers or tarsierlike animals, and had come into existence about 60 million years ago.[6] He therefore rejected the idea of such "missing links" as the australopithecines with their combination of apelike and hominid characteristics. Additional finds and further studies slowly converted most of the other doubters.

Broom, though he was eighty, was eager at the end of the war to resume the search for more australopithecines. Smuts offered him all the support he might need. However, when the premier left the country on a long trip, the Historical Monuments Commission informed Broom that he could do no more work without a permit and that a geologist would have to be present to make certain that no damage was done by any blasting. Broom was outraged. Smuts, upon his return, apparently agreed with Broom and told him to "carry on."

Broom and his assistant John T. Robinson then resumed work at Kromdraai. When a permit arrived three months later it said nothing about operations at Sterkfontein. Broom's answer was to shift operations to the quarry. Within a few days he had some fine teeth and part of a baby's skull. The doctor felt better. Two weeks later a blast loosened a large chunk of breccia that at first looked unpromising. As the smoke cleared, however, a whole and a perfect skull stood revealed. "I have seen many interesting sights in my long life," said Broom. "This was the most thrilling of my experience."

The blast had split the skull in two and the lime crystals that lined the brain case sparkled like diamonds in the sun, but in the doctor's mind no diamonds could have matched the value of the two pieces of skull so neatly embedded in the big blocks of rock that held them. Even before the skull was cleaned and put together again — a minor matter — Broom pronounced it "the most valuable specimen ever discovered." It would have been difficult to prove him wrong. Broom bestowed a special name and rating on his find, *Plesianthropus,* and the adult female represented soon became known around the laboratory as Mrs. Ples.

Public excitement about the unusual find ran high. Mrs. Ples was not only a remarkably clear emanation of a long-unsuspected past; her discoverey had also broken the law. The doctor's flouting of the commission had become too obvious to ignore. An investigation was called for and made. It established that there were no rock strata at the place where Broom was working and that no damage had been done. Broom was issued a permit: "So they had to allow me to continue though under still absurd conditions to which I pay no attention," Broom huffily announced.

Broom felt that it was justification when he soon thereafter found a nearly perfect male jaw and, on August 1, 1948, a complete pelvis. Usage had ground down the canine tooth in the jaw until it was in line with the other teeth, exactly as in man. Similar wear is never found in the projecting fanglike canines of the male anthropoids.

The pelvis settled the most critical problem. It showed beyond all question that the apemen had walked upright, or nearly upright. Up to that time a few bits of leg bone indicating bipedalism were dismissed as human bone that had somehow become mixed with the ape remains. What was equally significant, for all of its human characteristics the pelvis was not entirely manlike. "What we can now say is that the pelvis is not in the least anthropoid, and that it is nearly, but not quite human," the doctor concluded.

Soon after a University of California expedition arrived in South Africa, and offered to finance the work if Broom would open up a new cave. A site at Swartkrans, another kopje just across the valley from Sterkfontein, was selected. True to form, within a few days Broom found another massive jaw. The teeth were so large and square, though they were human in conformation, that they suggested comparison with some of the giant teeth that had long been found in China.

The world's honors as well as its recognition, were coming to the intrepid and dedicated doctor. The Royal Society of South Africa held a major international scientific congress in his honor and published a Robert Broom commemorative volume. Many medals and degrees were conferred on Broom in the United States and Great Britain. His life was at its fullest when he died on April 6, 1951, at eighty-four.

Authority Settles the Issue

Professor Le Gros Clark had continued the studies he began in South Africa. By 1949, when he prepared a formal appraisal of the australopithecines for the *Yearbook*

Figure 4.3. *The African sites of major* Australopithecus *finds.*

of Physical Anthropology, the remains of some thirty individuals had been found. The young and the old were represented, males and females, and enough parts of the body for a reconstruction of the whole. Never before had anthropology had such a wealth of material.

In his summary Le Gros Clark said:

> From all of this material it is evident in some respects that [the australopithecines] were definitely apelike creatures with small brains and large jaws. Indeed, in the general proportions of the brain case and facial skeleton they represent a simian level of development not very different from that of the modern large apes.

97

But in the details of the construction of the skull, in their dental morphology, and in their limb bones, the simian features are combined with a number of characters in which they differ from recent or fossil apes and at the same time approximate quite markedly to the Hominidae.

Clark further held it "a reasonable inference" that the "astonishingly primitive hominids" either were in the main line of human evolution or were only slightly modified descendants of such a group.

Now virtually all doubts were resolved. One who yielded completely was the eminent Sir Arthur Keith:

> I was one of those who took the point of view when the adult form was discovered it would prove nearer akin to the living African anthropoids, the gorilla and the chimpanzee. . . . I am now convinced on the evidence submitted by Dr. Robert Broom that Professor Dart was right and I was wrong. The *Australopithecinae* are in or near the line which culminated in the human form.[7]

By all the evidence man was meeting his ancestors. They were creatures with apelike brains and humanlike bodies. Almost no one had anticipated that this was the way it would be. The exact reverse for man's entrance had been anticipated. For some it remained a shock and unacceptable.

Tools — Absence and Presence

A negative finding raised one problem for the South African investigators. In the twenty years of their intensive search no stone tool of any kind had been found in association with any of the apemen fossils. Stone tools from later periods abounded in the general area, but it began to look as though the apemen had not yet acquired the primary skill of man. With their small brains, many argued that this

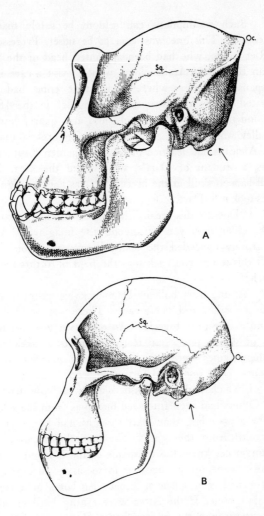

Figure 4.4. *The skull of a female gorilla (A) compared to that of a fossil man,* Australopithecus *(B). Note that in* Australopithecus *the anterior teeth are much smaller, as are all the parts of the skull associated with the jaw muscles.*

was to be expected. It was assumed that they lacked the mental capacity to conceive of tools or to work stone.

99

Such assumptions can seldom be safely made in archaeology. This one was soon to be upset. Professor C. van Riet Lowe, who had been appointed head of the South African Bureau of Archaeology, went to visit a cave in the Makapansgat Valley where a resistant tribe had been decimated during the Boer-native struggle in the 1850's. He found many Stone Age tools, and at a quarry lower in the valley some of the gray fossil-bearing breccia that the South Africans had learned often held apemen fossils. P. V. Tobias, a student of Dart's, who visited the area, found a fossil baboon skull in the breccia. It was another sign, and Tobias took it to Dart.

"Doesn't this mean," he asked, "that Makapansgat may be older than you or anyone else imagined?" When Dart readily conceded the point, Tobias went on, "And doesn't this tempt you back into the field of anthropological research?"

At the next holiday Dart took his entire anatomy class to the valley and its big caves. There was, as Dart said, "no end of the gray breccia." An operation was organized. Pieces of skulls, jaws, and teeth and parts of skeletons of australopithecines were found, as well as quantities of animal bones. Dart assembled forty-two baboon skulls, twenty-seven of which had been bashed in by a blow from the front. Others had been fractured by blows from the side and some by a pounding that Dart thought had been delivered "by stealth from the rear." The australopithecines, Dart was convinced, knew the technique of the bludgeon, and as his work went on he became increasingly sure that the bludgeon had been a heavy, knobby leg bone, or a jagged-edged jaw bone. If the latter were swung hard enough it could cut through the hardest bone. Dart decided that the apemen had used bone tools long before they learned to make stone tools.

With the aid of foundation grants, he made a detailed analysis of 7,159 fragments of bone, tooth, and horn taken from the Makapansgat breccia in one year of work. About 92 per cent of the bone came from various types of antelope. The australopithecines' favorite meat seemed to have been venison. As Dart continued with his sorting and compiling he found sharp-edged pieces of bone that he thought had been used for cutting and scraping. On the basis of his vast analyses of the fragments the doctor concluded that a Bone Age had preceded the Stone Age.

Once again he had created a controversy. Many of his fellow scientists questioned whether the australopithecine "bone tools" were actually tools or only bones broken by the gnawing of hyenas and other animals that had hauled the carcasses into their caves. One scientist collected an assemblage of bones from a modern hyena cave. An analysis showed that the bones had been broken and shattered in almost the same way as Dart's bone tools.

Dart answered that no hyena drove slivers of one bone into the core of another to split the heavier bone. He found several bones with such others wedged into them. The doctor devoted a chapter in his book *Adventures with the Missing Link* to the "hyena myth."

In 1954 Dr. C. K. Brain asked Dart's permission to make some soil tests in his dig at Makapansgat. When Brain returned from the cave he startled Dart by displaying 129 chipped, used, or damaged stones that he had found in an eighteen-foot sandy layer only twenty-five feet above the australopithecine-carrying gray breccia. The two immediately took them to the authority van Riet Lowe. Professor Lowe spread them out and soon separated 17 pebbles from the others. After careful study he told his co-workers, "I'm absolutely satisfied that these are pebble stone tools of the type I've already described from the highest gravel terraces of the Kafu and Kagera Rivers."

Only a few chips had been removed from the fist-sized stones. The rest of the stone was untouched, and only close scrutiny disclosed that the broken edges were not a normal breakage. But inspection left almost no doubt; this was handwork. Chips had been removed and a usable edge created by a living being who had acted deliberately and knowingly.

In a radio address that followed the announcement of the finding of the tools so close to the australopithecine layer, Professor Lowe said: "The discovery of the oldest recognizable man-made stone implements in deposits immediately over remains of manlike apes is of the greatest significance. It narrows the gap between ape and man as it has not been narrowed before."

But still the surprising tools had not been found in direct association with the australopithecines. That came soon afterward. Alun R. Hughes and Dr. Revil J. Mason came upon an australopithecine upper jaw as they were digging out several thousand pebble tools from the stratum where Brain had first found them.

The strange beings with the small brains and upright posture had quite evidently used their freed hands to shape stone to their own ends. No other living things before them had conquered the hardness of stone or discovered that by knocking two stones together in a certain way a tool could be created that would win food and safety. In the entire history of the world no other nonhuman animal had made a stone tool. The making of stone tools was one of the crucial discoveries of all time and a turning point for man. From the ape's stripping of a twig for termiting to the australopithecine's making of a stone pebble tool was a far cry. It might never have happened. But it did, and man was on his way.

While South Africa was startling the human world with the production of unexpected ancestors, Louis and Mary Leakey were carrying on the search for those forerunners in East Africa. It was a long search and for many years a futile one.

Leakey had been born in Africa. He was the son of English missionaries to the Kikuyu tribe and spoke Kikuyu as soon as he did English. After college in England where he specialized in prehistory, he returned to Africa in 1924 and soon became director of the Coryndon Museum in Nairobi.

He was only 500 miles away, but it took a week-

Figure 4.5. *A view of Olduvai Gorge.*

long drive over roadless wilds to reach the Olduvai Gorge. This 25-mile long gash in the earth — a part of the Great Rift Valley — was without much question one of the world's great repositories of fossils. Wilhelm Kattwinkel, the leader of a German expedition to Africa who had discovered it by nearly falling into it, had reported that fossils were present in an unimaginable profusion. He sensed that the 300-foot deep walls were literally a book of life. The record was there, from the beginnings at the floor of the gorge to the life of today on the Serengeti plains stretching back from the rim. When World War I halted German explorations and postwar difficulties prevented their resumption, some German scientists urged Leakey to take over.

Leakey needed no urging. He was more than eager to go, but until 1931 he lacked the financial backing for an expedition.

At Olduvai, during the dry season, water had to be carried from a spring some thirty-five miles away on the edge of the Ngorogoro Crater. At night Leakey counted the eyes of eleven lions shining in the darkness around his tents: "We never bothered them and they never bothered us," he always explained. But fossils were everywhere — a giant pig as big as a modern rhinoceros, pygmy animals, all animals long extinct. Ultimately Leakey counted more than 100 extinct species. But the only way to search for early man was largely on the hands and knees, crawling along the rough sides of the gorge to look for scraps of bone or tooth.

It was only possible to work in the semidesert area in the dry months — in the wet season downpours make it a quagmire — and the Leakeys, Louis and his wife Mary, could seldom afford to remain for more than seven weeks a year. But the Leakeys, accompanied in later years by their sons Richard and Jonathan, went back year after year. Neither heat, nor difficulty, nor discouragement stopped them. They were compiling a fossil record unlike any other in the world, and in this way twenty-eight years went by.

All the while in South Africa one find after another was being announced. The scientific fanfare was great, but for nearly the first thirty years the South Africans had found no stone tools with their apemen. It was frustrating. The Leakeys were finding numberless stone tools ranging from the simplest that must have been made by very early man to the most skillfully made, but they could find no sign of the makers of those simple early tools. It began to look as though early man had left his tools in one part of Africa and his bones in another. It was hard to understand, but the Leakeys never considered giving up.

On July 17, 1959, Leakey had developed a fever and had to remain in camp. But the day could not be lost. Mary, accompanied by two of the Dalmatians that always stood guard against snakes and intruding rhinos, went out to the place where they were working. As she crept up the hillside on hands and knees a bit of bone and then the glint of teeth caught her eye. Two teeth, brownish gray and almost iridescent, were just eroding from the rock. Even at first glance Mary Leakey could see that they were not animal teeth. Shaking with excitement, she made a little cairn of stones to mark the spot and ran for the Land Rover. She raced back to camp. As Leakey heard the speeding car, he jumped up in alarm. His first thought was that Mary had been bitten by a snake that somehow had slipped by the dogs.

Mary was running toward him, shouting "I've got him! I've got him!" Leakey understood instantly what she meant. His fever forgotten, the two jumped into the car and sped back to the site. As they knelt down to study the teeth shining against their dark background, he knew Mary was right. The teeth were nearly twice as wide as those of modern man, but they were clearly human in shape. The Leakeys had found the early man for whom they had been searching for twenty-eight years.

"I turned to look at Mary," said Louis, "and we almost cried with sheer joy, each seized by that terrific emotion that comes rarely in life. After all of our hoping and hardship and sacrifice we had reached our goal."

After photographs were made, the Leakeys went to work with camel-hair brushes and dental picks. To their added joy a palate lay behind the teeth and a partial skull. The expansion and contraction of the rock had cracked the fossil into more than 400 fragments. Some pieces were recovered by screening all of the scree, or fine rock debris, that lay around and on the slopes just below. The work took nineteen days.

While the task of putting the skull together went ahead — Leakey compared it to a complex three-dimensional jigsaw puzzle — the Leakeys continued to excavate the area around. A scene that was wholly unexpected was revealed. The skull had lain on what proved to be an ancient living floor or camp site on the edge of a lake that had long since disappeared. Lying about on the former beach were the bones of numerous small animals the campers had undoubtedly eaten, and nine of the pebble tools with which they probably had killed or skinned their prey. Even some of the chips that had been knocked off the rocks to make their jagged, sharp edges lay scattered here and there. Later many more tools were recovered.

The Leakeys had seen hundreds of such simple tools on the floor of the gorge and in its lowest strata, but never before — either at Olduvai, or in South Africa — had these beginning tools been so closely associated with their probable makers. Doubts that early man could have been a toolmaker were immediately lessened by the ancient scene the Leakeys had uncovered.

Leakey permitted his scientific imagination to reconstruct what might have happened on the day that somehow had been frozen into stone for millennia to come. Perhaps rain had fallen for many days and the lake level was rising ominously. The little band must have known that by dawn they would have to retreat. As they went to arouse an eighteen-year-old youth who had been ill for some time, they found him dead. Perhaps the hard-pressed campers covered his body with brush to protect it from the hyenas, and then fled to higher ground.

The rising water may quickly have covered the boy's body, the tools the hunters left behind, and the bones from their recent meals. A thick layer of silt from the muddy water settled over the whole scene. In the years that followed other rises of the lake deposited more and deeper silt on the mud-encased floor. Finally the lake itself vanished, leaving the boy and the campsite entombed under several hundred feet of sediments that were hardening into rock. Occasionally, volcanoes threw their ash and lava across the area.

The campsite might have remained forever buried if earthquakes had not convulsed the area and split it with a great crack that eroded into the gorge. The torrential rains that came at times even in that dry land continued to erode the sides of the canyon until at last the ancient campsite and its dead lay partly exposed at the face of the rock.

If the Leakeys had not come along when they did, the fossils and all the evidence of that lost day would soon have been washed anonymously into the gorge floor below.

The Leakeys tallied the animals on which the campers had fed — frogs, birds, a tortoise, some young pigs, a juvenile giant ostrich, rats, mice, lizards, and snakes. The selection indicated that even with their sharp-edged pebbles, the campers probably had been unable to attack giant and medium-sized animals of that time.

As the skull took shape — only the lower jaw was missing — the Leakeys saw an australopithecine type of being. Here was proof that the apemen had spread over large sections of Africa, for the gorge lay more than halfway up the eastern part of the continent from the australopithecine territory in the south.

But the skull and the face looking out at the reconstructors was much more like the big, massive apemen found originally at Swartkrans than like the small forms first found at Sterkfontein or Taung. It too was certainly robust. The huge molars that first had caught Mary Leakey's attention were at least twice the size of modern grinding teeth. They could have cracked nuts, and the Leakeys sometimes liked to call their discovery "nutcracker man." Detailed examination confirmed the humanlike shape of the teeth. The canines and incisors were reduced as they were in *Paranthropus robustus* and the third molars were relatively small as in *Australopithecus*.

The skull was low, as in the other apemen. But Leakey emphasized that the curve of the cheek and the general facial architecture showed advance toward *Homo*. He set up a separate genus and named the young man *Zinjanthropus boisei* (*Zinj* means East African in Arabic, and the *boisei* was for Charles Boise of London who helped finance the expedition).[8]

Leakey estimated the Zinj might be about 600,000 years old. His guess was based only on the generally accepted age of the period to which some of the animals belonged. It was about this time, however, that other precision methods of dating the past were being developed.

Radioactive carbon, or carbon-14, had been developed first and had made possible the exact dating of organic remains that were not more than about 50,000 years in age. A longer term clock was developed by using radioactive potassium, and measuring its decay into argon.

"If you were to carry 18 potassium atoms around in your pocket for approximately 1.2 billion years, you would find upon counting them that only half were left," said Dr. Garniss H. Curtis of the University of California, who with Dr. J. F. Evernden was an early developer of the method. "In place of the missing potassium atoms you would find eight calcium atoms and one argon atom."

The lava that had flowed over the *Zinjanthropus* site had contained potassium, as nearly all lavas do. Would it also contain argon? The California scientists went out to Africa to collect samples, and made measurements showing that the lava flow had occurred about 1,750,000 years ago. *Zinjanthropus* and the beach camp were not 600,000 years old, but 1,750,000! The anthropological world was startled again. Much rethinking had to be done.

In the meanwhile the Leakeys, with increased aid from the National Geographic Society and foundations, were expanding their operations. In a stratum about a foot below the Zinj level they made another discovery of first importance. They found a fossilized left foot that had walked on the earth at least 1,750,000 years ago. It was the first direct evidence in the foot of how man had evolved from quadruped to biped. The foot was nearly complete with five toe bones — only the toe tips were missing — the five middle foot bones, an ankle bone, and part of the heel.

F. Clark Howell of the University of California, Berkeley, lined up a model of the foot with a modern man's foot and a modern gorilla foot. The big toe of the gorilla projected almost at a right angle. That of the fossil foot lay in line with the others, like the toes of man. There were differences, however, particularly in the joining of the toes and in the curves of some bones. But essentially the foot from nearly 2 million years ago could have slipped into a modern shoe if the shoe were wide enough. The foot was nearly, but not quite human. These creatures of the past undoubtedly had brains no larger than those of the ape, but their feet, and the posture these indicated, were largely those of men. This discovery confirmed the deductions made from the pelvis found in South Africa.

"It helps to confirm Charles Darwin's theory of the evolution of the human race," commented Howell, in reference to Darwin's theory that the upright stance and the development of the feet came first.

The ancient beach deposit where the footbone had somehow survived the ages also held six finger bones — the first found for dawn man — two ribs, and fragments of a skull of a ten-year-old child.

Further testifying to the great age and rarity of the site was a wealth of animal fossils. Some, Leakey reported, came from genera and species never previously known on this earth. Others were from species he had not previously seen at Olduvai.

In the early 1960's the Leakeys found parts of several skulls, teeth, bone fragments, tools, and another living floor in the same area. The child from the "foot" level and the others, Leakey decided in collaboration with Tobias and J. R. Napier, had a larger brain and more skilled hands than the massively built nutcracker *Zinjanthropus*, or *A. boisei*. They named him *Homo habilis*.

Leakey had initially assumed that the tools on the campsite were made by the *Zinjanthropus* or *A. boisei* band. After finding *Homo habilis*, he proposed instead that they might have been made by the man of the larger brains and better hands. That would have put two species, one more advanced than the other, in the same area at the same time.

Other authorities did not agree. "I do not find it possible to concur," said Le Gros Clark.

In all its skeletal characters *Homo habilis* appears to correspond much more closely with the australopithecine group of early hominids. The cranial capacity has been estimated by Tobias to have been about 680 cc. This estimate, however, is based on two bones of the cranial roof, both of which are cracked, fragmented, and incomplete, and even if this is accepted as an accurate estimate it still comes within the gorilla range, as well as within estimations of the probable range of the australopithecines and certainly well below the cranial capacity of any known specimen of *Homo*.[9]

Le Gros Clark pointed out too that the foot was not yet human, that the finger bones "agree very well with" a thumb bone found at Swartkrans, and that Robinson, the best authority on the teeth, found no distinctive features to set the *habilis* teeth aside from those of the australopithecines. Clark suggested that *habilis* at most might be considered a "geographical variant," differing from the South African apemen only in minor ways.

More remains of the creatures of the distant past continued to come from the Leakeys in East Africa and from all the South African sites, Sterkfontein, Kromdraai, Swartkrans, and Makapansgat. A sizeable population that had lived over several millions of years was emerging from the ancient caves and campsites.

Alan Mann of the University of Pennsylvania went to Africa to study and total the amazing fossil heaps collecting in the South African area. To determine exactly how many individuals the bones represented was difficult, for some of the fragments might have come from one or from several individuals. On the basis of the most careful appraisal he arrived at these figures.

	Maximum	*Most probable*
Sterkfontein	88	50
Kromdraai	6	6
Swartkrans	192	100
Makapansgat	40	20
Totals	326	176

The totals, however, change constantly. None of the sites is more than partially investigated and the work continues.

What is important is that many individuals are represented and that they come not from one but from five sites in South Africa. The number of specimens might be compared with the eight from Java and the eleven from Peking. This is a wealth of material.

All living things and all living groups vary. In modern populations the measurement of thousands, particularly in schools and armies, produces a range of characteristics for each group. When only one skull or a very few are dug from the earth from some remote time, the one or the few generally are accepted as representative of a whole species or even genus. The discoverer as he studies his specimen also tends to be aware of its difference. There may be no others with which to compare it, or the man working out in a distant desert may not have the opportunity to make detailed comparisons. In anthropology, the genera proposed by the discoverers have tended to multiply. Most bear formidable names.

As the apeman material increased the scholars came in to classify and compare. Many skulls that seemed unique to the man who found them were held by the classifiers to be only variations in a general population. The verdict of the scholars was that all the apemen belong to one or possibly two species, a group that endured for some millions of years over wide territories. Some apemen may have differed locally, as modern races differ, but all were assigned to the one or two species, as all living men, however they may vary in appearance, are all made members of the species *Homo sapiens*.

Le Gros Clark, the outstanding authority, provisionally accepted the two species: *Australopithecus africanus,* a small general type, and *Australopithecus robustus,* the heavily built one.

"As an approximate parallel," he said, "one may refer to the pygmy chimpanzee and the more robust common type of chimpanzee that live on either bank of the Congo, or to the forest gorilla and the mountain gorilla that are nearly neighbors in Central Africa."

111

Clark also compared the two to modern man and the heavier, more massive-jawed Neanderthal man who flourished and then became extinct, both of which are *Homo sapiens:*

> The skull of the robust type shows quite pronounced contrasts with the gracile [slighter] type. For example, the brow ridges are more heavily built . . . the jaws are more massive, and the grinding teeth are large in size. The skull is also characterized, like that of the gracile type, by many of the same hominid features. The parallel with Neanderthal man and the modern type of man is certainly very apt. . . . It is a matter of discussion whether these two australopithecine types are to be regarded taxonomically as separate distinct species, or whether, after all, they are no more than two distinct subspecies or varieties of the same species.[10]

Regardless of the ultimate classification, the experts generally agree that the robust population was the one left behind. These heavy-set apemen remained in the more heavily forested areas while their smaller, less massive contemporaries, the *A. africanus,* pushed farther out onto the savannah and the way that led to man.

The australopithecines, all the evidence shows, had brains in the 450 to 550 cc range (modern man's brain is 1,250–1,550 cc; the gorilla's, 350–650 cc). They walked partly upright, perhaps with a shambling half-run, and made simple chipped stone tools. They flourished over wide, dry areas, very different from the jungles of their ancestors. They certainly had ranged from South Africa to East Africa. Did they go farther?

Ethiopia

There was no answer until the late 1960's. About a thousand miles north of Leakey's dig at Olduvai is a fossil-rich area in Ethiopia. In a low area at the north end of Lake

Rudolf, fossil bone lay scattered thick around the dry dusty surface and protruded from the faces of the low hills. An early report was made in 1891, and in 1896 an expedition verified the fossil wealth before it was turned back by sickness.

Far in the past the Lake Rudolf system had been connected with the Nile system — some of the fish remain the same into the present. After separation, the lake and the Omo River that fed into it often overflowed. In other eras the waters had retreated, but a rich animal life existed on the beaches and in the swamps. With its game and water, the area might also have been one to attract early man. Scientists were eager to investigate one of the great nearly unexplored fossil banks of the world.

Until the 1960's Emperor Haile Selassie refused all who wanted to go in, but he followed the discoveries in East and South Africa. Leakey finally was able to convince him that Ethiopia too should be opened to science. The emperor agreed to welcome an international expedition.

The International Palaeontological Research Expedition to the Omo Valley was the result. It was made up of French, Kenyan, and United States teams under the respective leadership of C. Arambourg, Richard E. F. Leakey, son of Louis and Mary Leakey, and Howell of the University of California. Work began in 1967.

A camp was set up near Lake Rudolf. By 11 A.M. the temperature was 108 to 110 degrees. The only way to describe the heat was "hotter than hell." The scientists worked from dawn to early afternoon and from late afternoon to dark. A shuttle plane brought supplies from Nairobi — about 750 miles away — and a helicopter assisted in the mapping of the area and in locating promising places. It also took the men back and forth to some of the places they were working.

Areas of potential interest seemed to be almost everywhere. The expedition listed 115 localities with fossils, all except two in an area of about twenty square miles.

"Many of the fossils were exposed at the surface," said Howell. "If we did not get to them they would disappear in the next big rain. It was a matter of crawling along and examining them."

In two years of work more than eighty species of animals were identified: elephant, rhinoceros, hippopotamus, giraffe, lion, monkey, rodent — and man.

Perfectly preserved teeth, some quite unworn, were found at the White Sands and Brown Sands locations, as well as many pieces of fossil bone.

The teeth and bones the scientists were scratching from the dry Ethiopian earth were, to their great interest and reward, australopithecine. So *Australopithecus* had been in northeast Africa as well as in the east and the south. His range — and the story of evolution — was being expanded in another giant leap.

The hot Ethiopian land was yielding even greater surprises. Some of the teeth seemed to be close in size and structural details to Leakey's *Homo habilis*. Others resembled *robustus,* and others *africanus,* the small gracile form originally found at Taung and Sterkfontein. One tooth, which had just erupted when its owner died — only a tiny patch of wear was shown — had erupted in a pattern that essentially duplicated the tooth of *africanus.*

In every case, however, there were differences as well as resemblances to the apemen in other parts of Africa. Until the expedition could find more material, Howell suggested that no final attempt should be made to determine the species of the apemen of the teeth and bones.

The river and lake deposits that held the australopithecine remains had been overspread several times by volcanic ash and lava, which meant that potassium-argon dates could be obtained. Samples sent to the dating laboratories yielded exciting reports — one stratum had been laid down nearly 3 million years ago. Just below it lay some teeth and a jawbone fragment of the early inhabitants. The apemen of the Omo then were at least 3 million years old. And some nearby beds showed dates of about 4 million years.

Suddenly the time set for the first creatures to leave the forests and make their way into the open lands was nearly doubled. The evolution of man was placed in a new time

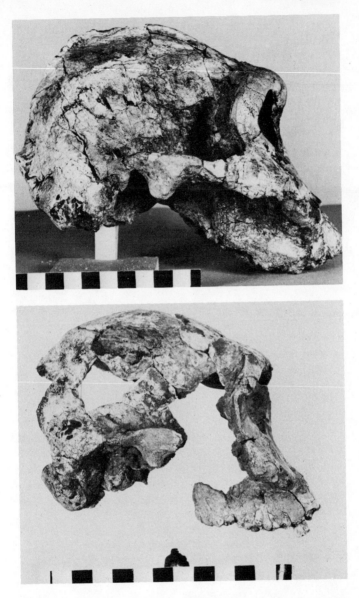

Figure 4.6. *Two skulls found by Richard E. Leakey in an area east of Lake Rudolph, Kenya. These skulls probably represent the male (top) and female of* Australopithecus.

perspective, and the scientists began new appraisals and calculations.

If the australopithecines were spread from south to northeast Africa at least 3 million years ago and if the dates of their separation from ape to man were set at 5 million to 10 million years, the gap from ape to man was growing very narrow. Few links were any longer missing.

What man had been at nearly every stage could now be seen. From ape to apeman — it was a long but steady and little interrupted progression. It had by all indications been accomplished in a few million years.

5

Becoming Human

It took the next 3 million to 4 million years to become human.

Change came as slowly then as biological change still does today. The twentieth century did not develop men capable of flying to the moon; its scientists invented the rockets and capsules — the systems — that permitted humans to overcome their natural inability to lift themselves unaided more than a few feet above the surface of the earth.

The apemen — the australopithecines — moving out onto the savannah with their newfound uprightness changed in two related ways. Natural selection favored those best able to adapt to the new dry land — to find food, to win battles, and to leave offspring who inherited the

119

advantageous characteristics of the parents. It was this, rather than having a foot with the big toe in alignment, that counted. But as those with a better adapted foot or pelvis produced the future generations, the foot and the pelvis changed too, though slowly, very slowly. Behaviors leading to reproductive success determined the fate of populations.

It was a way of life that evolved.

But all that remained of the past, except for the DNA transmitted to all descendants, were the bones. The bones blasted from ancient cave deposits or dug from the beaches of the past are the only visible evidence of what the apemen had been.

To learn how these apemen of 4,000,000 years ago evolved to 500,000 years ago when *Homo erectus* (early man) appeared, science had to reconstruct the populations spreading out across the dry lands of Africa and perhaps farther on.

How could a human possibly have been derived from apes — apes that lived in a limited forest territory, that were primarily vegetarians and gatherers, that foraged for themselves and ate what they found where they found it, that were essentially nomads without a fixed base or home, that were dominated by the big males, whose females were receptive only during estrus, whose young were not taught but had to learn by watching and in play? How did the intelligent and inquisitive apes turn into hunters, meat eaters, world travelers, and cooperative individuals? How did families, the continuous receptivity of the female, and the training of the young come into being? How did apemen become human?

Achieving a Unique Way of Life

Other questions had to be answered about this long stretch of history. Again, and most particularly, why did only one group, and no other, make the transition? How did one group that had broken away from the other apes become man?

From the australopithecines on, certainly, the answers had to be sought in the unique way of life that was evolved, and how this changed or did not change the apemen physically and biologically.

The fossils, of course, supplied one clue to the biggest change ever made by any living group. Studying the living populations of apes yielded another part of the answer, for some had made little change in the ancestral way of life from which the apemen had departed. The new biochemical studies also were drawn upon again for information about what had changed and what had not.

If what evolved was successful behavior, understanding of the evolution of the species still could be achieved only by the reconstruction of the behaviors of past populations. But the more well-dated fossils that are available and the more that is known of the behavior of living primates, the more reliable the reconstruction of the past can be.

Well before the apemen moved out of the forest they may have used tools. At what point the ape's waving or throwing of a branch or a stone became a regular or an aimed wielding of these weapons no one can yet say. No timed evidence shows when the chimpanzee's stripping of a twig to make a tool for termiting turned into using a chunk of rock to pry or to break open a nut.

Experiment confirmed the huge advantage that a stone tool gives to its user. Held in the hand it can be used for pounding, digging, or scraping. Flesh and bone can be cut with a flaked chip and what would be a mild blow with the fist becomes lethal with a rock in the hand. If monkeys would use a stick or stone to dig out the roots they like, they could double their food supply.

Exact data also is lacking on when the great apes' carrying of a stick or piece of fruit in one hand during knuckle-walking changed into an upright walk or shuffle that permitted sticks or fruit to be carried in both hands.

It was clear, nevertheless, that bipedalism freed the hands for a wide variety of skills. It made possible the human way of life. This point of view may be stated in the following way:

In many populations of apes over some millions of years minimal tool-use was present. In some of these populations the carrying of tools and the products of tool-use became so important that selection favored those groups of apes in which bipedal locomotion was most efficient. Bipedalism permitted the evolution of skillful, practiced tool-use which, in turn, became more effective as the locomotor pattern evolved responding to the new demands. Thus, locomotion and tool-use were both cause and effect of each other.

Tool-use did not result from a preceding bipedal adaptation, nor from a discovery that happened once. Tool-use probably developed through history repeating itself countless times in ape populations of several species over millions of years.

By the time the apemen had taken to life on the wide dry savannahs of South Africa or in the bush country of East Africa they had become tool-users and toolmakers.

The evidence of this new way of life is twofold — the tools themselves and the reduction of the canine teeth. All the australopithecines found so far, in south, east, and northeast Africa, have small canine teeth. Not one has the big slashing canine tusks of the apes. Without the canines and without other defenses, such as speed or ruse, the apemen would not have survived very long on the savannah. They would have been easy prey for the carnivores, and the small canines are proof in themselves of reliance on tools and weapons.

Well before 3 million years ago — though the date is an estimate — the apemen of South Africa had learned to make and use pebble tools. They carried pieces of quartz and chert from the beaches of nearby rivers to their caves. Nearly three-fourths of the pebbles were not worked at all. If there had been any similar stones in the caves where they were found, they could not have been identified as tools. But the hard brown quartz does not occur in the former caves. It had to be carried in, purposefully, by a creature who wanted it sufficiently to lug it for a considerable distance.

Some pebbles must have broken when they were used for pounding, and it was then not a difficult discovery to see that the jagged edges could help to skin a small animal. To skin an animal with the teeth and fingernails alone is nearly impossible, as Leakey once demonstrated. When he knocked a few chips from a rock and used the sharp edge to strip away the skin, he had the meat in a few minutes.

Some pebbles, though, were deliberately made into tools. When a rock was held with one hand and struck with another a chip was knocked off one side and then the other to produce an effective cutting edge.

J. Desmond Clark gives a course in prehistory at the University of California to afford graduate anthropology students an insight into the life of early man. With the guidance of their instructor, the students learn to make good pebble tools in a day. However, even in a full semester of work, no student has mastered the making of the fine stone tools that man made much later in his history (see Fig. 5.1).

At Olduvai the discovery of the living floor or camp-site of the *Zinjanthropus* band and its dating made it certain that the australopithecines were making stone tools at least 1.75 million years ago. Not only were numerous pebble tools found, but the hammerstone that had been used. Some chips of stone that had been struck off also showed signs of use. The sharp-edged chips were excellent for scraping or for digging the marrow from a bone.

In the early 1970's a comparable living floor, found by Richard Leakey at Lake Rudolf, was dated almost a million years earlier, or at about 2.6 million years ago. The dated beginnings of tool-use were rolled back that much farther.

The Hand and Its Use

The hand that made the sharp-edged pebble tools was, as the discovery of the bones proved, a hand between that of an ape and a human. Though relatively small, the proportions of the digits and the palm were much the same

123

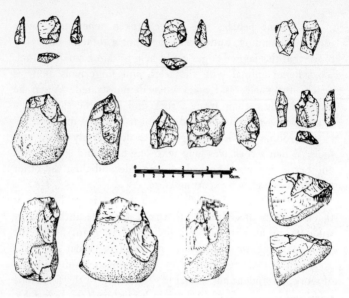

Figure 5.1. *Tools of the Oldowan Industry from Bed I, Olduvai Gorge (above), which have been dated to 1.75 million years ago, are contrasted with the Upper Acheulian tools from Kalambo Falls (opposite page) which have been dated to 60,000 years before the present and earlier. The primitive Oldowan tools, which are made from quartz and lava, contrast with the specialized tools of the Acheulian period, which are made from chert (the small size) and from quartzite (the larger).*

as in man. The tips of the terminal bones of the fingers were quite wide and the finger tips must have been broad. The fingers were somewhat curved.

John Napier, who studied the Olduvai hand and the evolution of the hand, pointed out that the Olduvai hand would have been capable of a tremendously strong power grip, perhaps stronger than that of modern man. (In the power grip, a tool like a screwdriver is held in the palm with the fingers flexed around it and the thumb applying counter pressure. Essentially a whole-hand grip, it is used when strength is needed. The other basic grip, the precision, is used when accuracy and delicacy of touch are

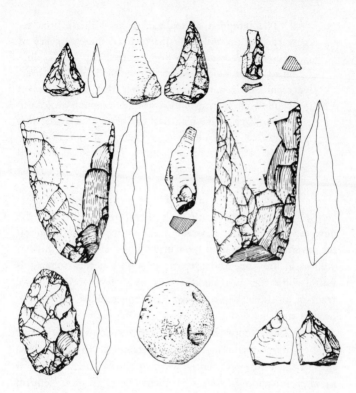

required. A tool like a pencil is held between the tips of one or more fingers and the fully opposed thumb — it is basically a finger grip.)

The australopithecine thumb probably was short and angled something like the thumb of the gorilla. Although it would have been opposable, Napier doubted that this thumb could perform the actions of the modern precision grip.

> The Olduvai hand would have had little difficulty in making the tools that were found with it. I myself have made such pebble tools applying only the power grip to hold and strike two stones together.

125

The inception of toolmaking has hitherto been regarded as the milestone that marked the emergence of the genus *Homo*. It has been assumed that the development was a sudden event, happening as it were, overnight. It is now becoming clear that this important cultural phase in evolution had its inception at a much earlier stage in the biological evolution of man and that it existed for a much longer period of time and that it was set in motion by a much less advanced hominid and a much less specialized hand than has previously been believed.[1]

Making and using tools therefore was part of the new way of life the australopithecines were taking up on the savannah. They used tools instead of teeth in fighting, as well as in hunting, and preparing food. Yet the stone tools found with the australopithecines must have been only a fraction of their tools. Sticks and bones must have been used as well.

The chimpanzees, as the van Lawick-Goodall work showed, made termiting sticks and sponges. However, these acts in the forest apparently were not sufficiently important to alter selection pressures in their favor. In the plentiful world of the forest capturing termites and recovering water from a pocket in a branch did not determine survival or death. Only when populations moved out into the dry lands was using and making tools vital.

Meat-eating

On the savannah there were few fruit trees and not so many of the succulent herbs in which the forest abounded. But small game were profuse. The great apes had always eaten meat with great eagerness and relish when they happened to kill a young antelope or a hare in some forest clearing. They also had occasionally joined to hunt and kill a monkey, and after the leading captor had eaten his fill he sometimes would give some of the meat and bones to others in the troop. But the apes were primarily vegetarians and the hunting was occasional and often seemed to be a matter of chance.

With the australopithecines the old pattern was reversed. The bones around the sites where they camped or lived showed that they ate whatever animals they could capture and kill. At the same time they did not totally abandon the old vegetarian diet. The heavy, grinding molars of *Zinjanthropus* indicate that he and his fellows ate roots and coarse vegetation. Life however began to center around meat and hunting.

Some have suggested that the australopithecines may have started their meat-eating as scavengers, seizing what they could after the lions had made the kills. The studies of the modern great apes throw this theory into question. Both chimpanzees and gorillas ignore a carcass lying on the ground. Only when they make a kill do they eat meat. Nothing indicates that the apemen with their simple stone tools could have driven a lion away from his kill or could even have routed the hyenas or vultures moving in after the lions had left. Scavenging would have brought the australopithecines into direct conflict with large animals they could not beat.

The australopithecines then had to hunt for their food in the semidesert lands into which they had moved. With a stone in hand an australopithecine was well equipped to kill a small or young animal. The stone could crack open a small skull as an empty fist never could. Or a stone thrown, either underhand or overhand, might hit and cripple an animal to make the capture much easier.

Studies of the baboons have shown how another animal taking up life in the same dry open lands makes similar adaptations. The baboons, among the few monkeys that have moved to the ground, also became partial meat-eaters and hunters. They made no progress in learning to use tools, but the big powerful males learned to hunt in groups. They surround their prey and block its escape. With their big strong canines they can dispatch almost any small animal.

The presence of a little band at Olduvai with the game they had eaten indicated that the australopithecines may have also turned to group hunting. When an animal was killed the apemen may have carried it or dragged it back to their campsite.

In contrast, the baboons neither carry nor store food. Carrying is so awkward for quadrupeds that they transport nothing in the hands for more than a few yards, though they may occasionally carry food or some other object in the mouth or under the arm. One observer once saw a baboon toss an object ahead, pick it up, and toss it again.

The presence of stones in Sterkfontein which had been carried for miles from a river gravel is evidence for bipedalism and the structure of the australopithecine pelvis supports this inference. It is hard to believe that animals which carried stones did not also carry food and thus initiate an important stage in freeing man from the necessity of eating his food where he found it.

The Australopithecines and Water

The ability to carry water would greatly increase mobility. Terrestrial monkeys, such as baboons, must stay within about two miles of water.

When the australopithecines went to the river to gather stones and possibly to hunt animals along the banks, they did not seem to gather shellfish or fish. The consumption of shellfish leaves huge middens that tend to last indefinitely when a site is buried, and none have been found.

Except for drinking at the edge of a stream, water was a danger. To learn to swim, the bipedal apemen would have had to master a difficult skill. Unlike the quadrupeds the bipeds cannot swim naturally. The quadrupedal monkey, like a dog, can keep afloat with its normal running movements, and thus does not have to learn a new motor habit to swim. This began to change with the apes. Their normal patterns of movement will not keep them above the water's surface, and Schaller saw that gorillas will not cross even a narrow stream if they have to enter the water. Water must have also been a barrier for the apeman. Though he went to the edge, he stayed out and did not extend his hunting into the stream.

Farther Afield

Hunting began to take the apemen farther afield. Most of their primate ancestors lived their entire lives in a range of 4 or 5 square miles. Monkeys have excellent vision and from the treetops they undoubtedly can see fruit trees and promising land much beyond their own range. Whatever the lure they do not go. Scientists have tried to drive baboons outside their range, but when the animals approach the boundaries they become uneasy and excited. If driven farther, they loop back to their familiar land.

The apemen with their stones in hand ventured farther to get enough meat to satisfy their needs. Not until agriculture came in several million years later could man live on a small piece of ground.

How much territory is necessary for a hunter is demonstrated by the Bushmen of Africa. One area of 600 square miles with 11 water holes supports 240 hunters, while in a nearby preserve about 250 baboons live in a few square miles around one water hole. In Australia bands of about 35 aborigine hunter-gatherers occupied home ranges of 150 to 750 square miles. Constant hunting, by humans or animals, rapidly depletes the game in a small area. The 40 square miles of Nairobi Park, for example, support an average population of only 14 lions as compared to 400 baboons.

The wider areas beckoning the apemen also gave them access to more seasonal foods and to more potentially useful materials, important for increasing tool-use. The pebble tools showed that the apemen went a considerable distance to find rocks of the right size, form, and material. They may also have gone to more than one stream to make their selection.

Wood also had to be found. When wood became

Figure 5.2. *Even primates as large as baboons must seek safety from large carnivores in trees. On the open savanna, protection from predators is a major problem for contemporary primates, as it must have been for ancient man. The baboons in this photograph taken at Nairobi National Park, Kenya, have climbed a thorn tree to avoid the lioness.*

something more than a tree to climb, hardness and texture counted. If a stick was to be used, it had to be stiff and strong enough not to break at the first impact.

Availability of materials is critical to the tool-user, and early men must have had a very different interest in their environment from that of the monkeys and apes. The presence of tools in the archaeological record is not only an indication of technical progress, but also an index of interest in inanimate objects and in a much larger part of the environment than is the case with nonhuman primates.

In a small area the population must be carried on local resources, and natural selection favors biology and behavior that efficiently utilize these limited opportunities. In a wider area natural selection favors the knowledge that enables a group to utilize seasonal and occasional food sources.

Interest in a large area is human. When the australopithecines could walk 10 miles in a straight line they might be said to be human and unique.

Early Groups

The hunters who walked ten miles in a straight line (or it may have been a zigzag) in pursuit of some quarry were members of a group. Every campsite testifies to the presence of more than one or two individuals. Like all primates, the australopithecines then were intensely social, group-living creatures. Moreover, the group was a survival mechanism in itself.

Studies of the contemporary primates as well as the archaeological record supply some strong indications of the size of the australopithecine bands. Lee and De Vore believe that bands of hunters were small.[2] Kenneth Page Oakley suggests a range of 10 to 200. Such group sizes are common in the nonhuman primates.

The baboons, the other specialized savannah-dwellers, most frequently live in troops of 30 to 50. Such a group might have 5 to 10 adult males, 10 to 20 adult females, and an equal number of juveniles. One typical group near Victoria Falls was made up of 5 adult males, 12 adult females, 14 juveniles, and 2 infants. At the other end of the scale, the size of bands of primitive human hunters has been estimated to average from 20 to 50.

It appears that the size of the band did not increase greatly and could not until after agriculture. The human way of life does not necessarily result in an increase in the size of the local group.

The anthropologists also put the comparison in

131

Figure 5.3. *A baboon troop in march position* (*above*) *and being threatened by a leopard* (*opposite page*).

terms of population density. In Nairobi Park there are about 10 baboons per square mile and in other parts of Africa the density is believed to be greater. But preagricultural man, the studies indicate, would need 5 to 10 square miles per person.

In other words, troops of baboons may exceed in size the bands of primitive hunters, and the density of baboons may reach a hundred times that attributed to ancient man. Even today there are more baboons than Masai in the Masai Reserve.

In the little australopithecine bands the ape way of life changed into a new human way. Membership in the group directly influenced survival and reproduction. The group offered protection against predators, help in finding food and water, and a way to cope with injury and illness. It also facilitated the production of young and their care and training.

The base was established much earlier. Without his group a lone primate had a very poor chance of surviving. The group literally meant life or death. Once a band began

living on the ground, the much greater danger from predators would alone be sufficient reason for a strictly organized social system.

Observers often watched primate groups moving through the forest. Any animal unable to keep up with the group soon disappeared, presumably captured and eaten by predators. The young and the sick or injured were in particular danger if they became separated.

When the troop moved out on the daily round all members had to move with it, or be deserted. Sick and wounded animals often made great efforts to keep up with the troop, but finally fell behind. In one case at least three of these were killed. In wild primates, injuries are common, and animals so sick that they can be spotted by a relatively distant human observer are frequent. For a wild primate a fatal sickness is one which separates it from the troop.

An infant separated from its mother and the troop had almost no chance of surviving. Only those who succeeded in staying with the troop lived to pass on their skills to offspring.

If an attack were made on a troop of apes the males moved out to meet it. The females and young took shelter in the trees if any were available. The troop also guarded against surprise. As they moved across country the mature and dominant males walked at the front and rear of the group. At the center were the mothers and babies. The moment a female gave birth to an infant she moved into the sheltered center position. The very young pressed close around the mothers and babies, and the juveniles scampered along the sides, though well within the screen of the mature males.

When the australopithecine descendants of the apes took to fighting with stone tools instead of teeth, there is no indication that the role of the male as the protector and the fighter changed. It was also the male who went hunting and first pushed on beyond the psychological boundaries that always had halted all other primates.

The female australopithecines became gatherers. They apparently picked fruits and roots and brought them back to the camp or cave for the others to share. And thus another human change was occurring. This had not generally happened before. Except for nursing her infant, the female ape, like the male, ate her food where she found it. As soon as the infant was weaned, it had to gather food for itself, even though it remained in the company of the mother. Only the chimpanzee will sometimes share a choice bit with an infant or help an infant pick a piece of fruit. Jane van Lawick-Goodall watched Fifi sitting immediately in front of David Graybeard and imploringly begging for a piece of his banana or sometimes for some food he was chewing. Her hand was held out in a pleading gesture and her whole yearning, concentrated expression asked for a share. And sometimes she got it. David was photographed tearing off pieces of cardboard on which he loved to chew to give them to any female who came up and whimpered for a bit.

When Jane van Lawick-Goodall began to serve bananas, the dominant males took them all. She was forced to design her intricately operated boxes to insure a share for all. Only then did Flo and the youngsters get the prized fruits.

Sharing, the Human Way

The change to a hunting and carrying way of life changed this general winner-take-all or nearly all to a more human pattern. At first, as in some primitive hunting societies, the hunters may have eaten some game at the point of capture. With a stone tool, though, they could cut away some meat to carry back to the camp. The bones found on the living floors probably represented only a small part of the animals that were killed. If the whole carcass had been dragged back, the bone middens or garbage dumps would have been much larger than they were. Whether the females had found anything equivalent to a basket for bringing back fruits and leaves has not been determined.

The new hunting was a set of ways of life. It involved a division of labor between male and female, sharing according to custom, cooperation among males, planning, knowledge of many species and large areas, and technical skill. Sharing both in the family and in a wider society is fundamental.

Human hunting as a whole social pattern has been compared to the hunting of wolves rather than apes or monkeys. But this completely misses the special nature of human adaptation. Human females do not go out to hunt and then regurgitate to their young when they return. Human young do not stay in dens, but are carried by their mothers. Male wolves do not kill with tools, butcher, and share with females who have been gathering. A human mother who hunted like a wolf or wild dog would have to run a two-minute mile carrying a baby. In an evolutionary sense the whole human pattern was new. The success of the human way dominated evolution and determined the relation of biology and culture for thousands of years.

Dominance

Ways of living together began to change — perhaps had to change — when australopithecine hunters brought food back to the caves. Social relationships in all the primate groups always had been complex. But most groups in the past were hierarchies dominated by one or a few mature males. Each member had his place and knew it. The new primate studies have disclosed, however, that none of the primate societies were the "primal hordes" Sigmund Freud theorized in his picture of a troop as a horde in which a single aggressive male monopolized the female and drove out his sons.

In baboon troops dominance is based on the ability to fight. But once established, the dominant animal's position generally is recognized by all others. Only occasionally does the dominant have to enforce the right submissive response by a bite or a chase. Generally a big silver-backed male gorilla has only to nudge another member of the troop to keep him in line. Most chimpanzees also make the proper crouching, half-bending turn of the back that signifies submission. The crouch is used generally when subordinates come into close proximity to a high-ranking chimpanzee. When all goes well, the dominant may then reach out to give a reassuring touch or even embrace.

However, Mike, the highest ranking chimpanzee in the Gombe troop, seemingly won his position by learning to make an unholy amount of noise. He discovered how to seize an empty kerosene can and drag it behind him. As it bounced over the ground at Mike's breakneck speed, the other chimps hurried to get out of the way. Mike then mastered the art of keeping as many as three empty cans in front of him as he charged. When he and the horrendous noise stopped, even the mighty Goliath hurried up to bow to him. Crouching to the ground Goliath kissed and groomed Mike to acknowledge Mike's new supreme status. Even though Jane van Lawick-Goodall later wearied of the noise and deprived Mike of his noisemaking cans, he kept his position as the most feared and respected in the troop. High-ranking females also received crouches and bobs from lower-ranking females as well as from some juveniles.

Sometimes the dominance hierarchies in chimpan-

Figure 5.4. *Figan (right) as a sign of submission presents his rump to the dominant Goliath (top photo). Goliath reassures Figan by touching him, and Figan gradually relaxes (bottom).*

zees were backed up by alliances between several males. The allies would quickly go into action together if trouble arose. The observers also saw a few alliances for power between a male and female.

The dominance arrangement usually reduced intra-group fighting to a minimum. One monkey group in the laboratories of the University of California lived peaceably under the dominance of one male. When he was removed, the peaceful old order continued for two to three weeks. Then the male who had stood second made his move to take over. Fights broke out and in the next few weeks several males received severe bites. The order then was settled again and peace returned under the new boss. Again every troop member knew his place.

Dominance usually has little effect on food-gathering. The normal spacing of a troop of gorillas or chimpanzees as they forage through the forest keeps the animals far enough apart for each to gather without interference with another. Only rarely does a dominant animal displace another from a choice place in a fruit tree.

The gathering and immediate eating of fruit, grass, and roots led to a noncompetitive economic life. This quiet noninterference changed rapidly, however, when Jane van Lawick-Goodall supplied the bananas. It probably changed in the same way when the use of tools and the transporting of food began.

Problems of distribution were created which could not be solved by a social system under the control of the larger animals. With the killing of large animals the problem of distribution must have become even more severe.

Although the carnivores share food, the australopithecine situation must have been much more complicated. If the troops had as many as 50 or 60 members, as some authorities have estimated, it meant that they all had to share the meat. No comparable situation exists among lions or other carnivores. The problem created was a new one. Tools, carrying, and hunting helped the apemen to survive the rigors of life on the savannah, but cooperation and sharing were also essential for survival.

With sharing, dominance very likely became less important in social control. If a dominant australopithecine had taken all the food, the rest of the troop might have perished in hard times, and the dominant could not have survived alone, or have left more offspring. Selection at last began to give the edge to cooperation. The troops that shared the meat became those which flourished and continued.

Cooperation Begins with Mother and Child

The base for such cooperation was laid within the troop by well-established relationships, most particularly by the relationship between mothers and offspring. Two continuing studies of Japanese and Indian macaques living free on the Caribbean island of Cayo Santiago show how genetic relationships play a major part in setting the course and nature of social interactions. The bonds between mother and infant persisted into adult life and often provided a nucleus for other social relations.

In the van Lawick-Goodall study, when Flint was born to Flo, his sister Fifi was fascinated and his two adolescent brothers, Figan and Faben, stared at him curiously and patted him occasionally. Fifi, though, would constantly quit her play to watch the baby and to beg her mother to let her take him. Not until the infant was about three months old did Flo let her hold him. With a look of wonderment that was recorded by the camera Fifi held him close and kept very still. After that she took the baby constantly, playing with him and grooming him. Flo rushed in only if she heard the infant whimper. At about six months, Flint took his first wobbly steps away from his mother. Even old J. B., whose temper was short, would reach out to pat or tickle him. Figan and Faben then also would play with him. The mother and her offspring of three different matings formed a steady group within the troop.

Two and a half years later, when Flo's next baby, Goblin, had been born, Jane van Lawick-Goodall heard the new infant whimpering and crying. He was hanging

from a branch, but his short, little legs could not reach the branch below. Flint who had earlier been playing with him heard the cries and hurried to the tree where his infant brother was marooned. He put his arms around Goblin's waist and gently helped him down.

By the time Figan and Faben were three years old, they still were frequently near their mother. Nevertheless Flo screamed and got out of the way when they put on one of their charging displays. When they were thirteen or fourteen the two young males were fully mature and had worked their way into the young males of the troop. But the ties with their mother and their brothers and sisters had persisted for a lengthy period.

Friendships within the group also were evident to the observers. Mr. Worzle was old and arthritic and was bullied by all the other males except when he accompanied his friend Leakey. In the presence of high-ranking Leakey, Mr. Worzle often became bold enough to attack some of his superiors.

"We wonder," said Jane van Lawick-Goodall, "if this and some of the other friendships may be founded on family relationships. Are Leakey and Mr. Worzle brothers? Certainly they have a similar mutation of the eyes. Mr. Worzle has eyes that resemble those of a man (white, rather than a dark cornea) and Leakey shares this startling feature. He has enough white in his eyes to give him something of Mr. Worzle's appearance.

"Perhaps the companionships between young siblings develop into the casual, but persistent friendships that we see between some of the adult chimpanzees."

When the genealogy was known, the observers also found that a group of four or five sitting together and grooming one another was likely to be related.

The relationships that continued into adult life may also have entered into dominance interactions. Dr. Donald

---

Figure 5.5. *The baby Flint reached from his sister Fifi to Figan (opposite, top). When Flo approached, Figan raised his arms as if to show he was not harming the infant (bottom).*

Sade saw a female rhesus monkey divert the attack of a dominant male from her adult son, and saw another adult female protect her juvenile half-sister (paternity is never determinable). Jane van Lawick-Goodall was watching once when Flo attacked another female, perhaps without noticing that her annoyer's adolescent son Pepe was feeding nearby. When Pepe heard his mother's screams, he quickly came to her help, and the two together put the bossy Flo to rout.

Young Melissa would hurry to one of the big males when any other chimp attacked her. She would stretch out a hand as though begging him to avenge her, and Jane van Lawick-Goodall reported that he often did.

The dominant males also showed affection for the infants. At times the big males would indulgently let the babies clamber all over them. They also would immediately go to the protection of the youngsters if any danger threatened. Above all they were kind to the little ones, giving them a pat now and then, chucking them under the chin, and sometimes playing with them.

Washburn, Jay, and Lancaster said in a paper on the subject:

> It should be stressed that there is no information leading us to believe that these animals are either recognizing genetic relationships or responding to an abstract concept of family. Rather these social relationships are determined by the necessarily close association of mother with newborn infant, which is extended through time and generations and which ramifies into close association among siblings.
>
> Because of their dramatic character, the importance of dominance and aggression has been greatly exaggerated compared to the continuing, positive affectional relations between related animals. It is expressed by their sitting and feeding together, touching and grooming.[3]

Far from being Freud's "primal horde" — an unruly group dominated by a tyrant — close affectionate relations existed between mother and offspring, between the youngsters playing together, and in friendships that flourished between males and sometimes between males and females. The base was well laid for a human social system. When hunting and bringing home the meat required cooperation and sharing instead of the old dominance pattern there were relationships on which sharing could be built. The little bands of man's ancestors were so constituted that social learning was not difficult.

"Monkeys and apes adapt by their social life and the group provides the context of affection, protection, and stability in which learning occurs," Washburn, Jay, and Lancaster continued. "Society is a major adaptive mechanism with many functions."

The Family

Another change went far to remake the old animal way of life. It opened the way for the family instead of the troop, if not the horde.

All that was needed to "derive a family" from the primate's well-knit society was some sort of a more lasting relationship between the male and the female.

The chimpanzees, the gorillas, the African monkeys, or any of the other primates have no such relationship. When the female chimpanzee goes into estrus or heat — about seven days in each thirty-four — she may at first mate with several young males of the troop. When the period is at its peak, however, she forms a temporary consort relationship with a mature male. At the end of estrus she moves back to her usual position in the center of the troop with the other females and the young. During estrus the female is a disruptive force in the troop. The ordinarily placid give-and-take relations are badly upset. Fights break out and the normal social pattern is disrupted.

Most of the fighting, however, is not over the female. It is not a question of one male being denied access to the female. It is just that the males are more aggressive at this time.

Andrew Wilson, who among others studied the monkeys on the island of Santiago, found that during the breeding season the death rate tripled.[4] Serious injuries also multiplied. The frequency of fighting increased sharply during the mating season and dropped immediately afterward.

Among the primates, sex is a disruptive, even a violent force. In addition during this period the male is a much more difficult creature to live with. There's a fundamental biology here which is exceedingly important.

However, sex had long been considered a major binding force in primate society. Some anthropologists maintained that sex alone had kept primate troops together during the years. The proponents of this view emphasized that breeding went on all through the year, and that there was no breeding season as such. New data established, however, that some monkeys confine sexual activity to one period of the year, and that in others the breeding season is well-marked. Among the Japanese macaques most mating occurred from November to March and births were concentrated in June and July. Nevertheless, the troops continued as an organized social unit during the whole year.

Further observation has identified sex as one of the forces that keep primates together, but the bond between individual and individual is much more fundamental and much deeper than sex. We are profoundly social with or without sex, and the emphasis on sexual activity as a social bond probably is greatly exaggerated in our society.

Among the primates, breeding seasons, along with estrus, meant a system of multiple mating. The father was never determinable and he took no economic or other responsibility for offspring. No evidence has been found that a father ever recognized his own child or that he associated sex with the production of infants. Though the males were tolerant of the young and even affectionate, it was a general affection and guardianship, rather than the father-and-child relationship of human society.

At what point estrus was lost in the primates coming down from the trees and moving out onto the savannah is unknown. The change must have happened early, perhaps along with the development of bipedalism.

If estrus were less marked in some females and if such females were more receptive to sex over longer periods of time, they may have been able to give better care to their infants. Observers have been unable to see any way in which estrus behavior can be combined with continuing care of dependent offspring. Therefore, if infants with better care were most likely to survive and produce offspring of their own, estrus behavior could well be lost. The disruptive effect of the cycle on the social life of the troop and the dangerous in-fighting it produced may have speeded its loss and the substitution of continuing sexual receptivity in the female. Certainly the physiology of the female was radically modified and control of behavior by the ductless glands was greatly reduced.

The loss of the uncontrollable sex drive proved a crucial change because the human type of family could replace multiple mating. In effect, it became possible to add a male to the already existing mother-plus-young social group of monkeys and apes. Hunting in turn made the added male the provider of meat or, in anthropological terms, brought in economic reciprocity, which created another new set of interpersonal bonds. According to this view, the human family resulted from the reciprocity of hunting and the addition of a male to the mother-plus-young social group.

The changes in the way of life and the social system had to be accompanied by one other essential change. As the ape brain surpassed the monkey brain in size, infants had to be born more and more immature in order to be born at all. A more mature infant with a larger brain and head could not have passed through the mother's birth canal.

Monkeys and apes are born with the ability to cling to the mother's hair. A monkey mother must constantly move to gather food and to keep up with the troop. For this she must have unfettered use of the hands and feet. Unless the infant can cling tight while she runs and jumps, it almost certainly perishes. Its mother cannot hold it.

145

The knuckle-walking chimpanzee and gorilla mothers can help the baby to cling during its first few weeks, though only with great difficulty. We have mentioned the baboon mother who tried to hold a weak infant as she walked along. Attempting to get along on three legs she was so handicapped that she fell far behind the troop and probably would have been lost if a male had not stayed to protect her.

But the later australopithecine mother was nearly hairless, and her infant was not born with the motor development for clinging. The freedom of her hands solved the dilemma of supporting the baby. As these human ancestors became increasingly bipedal the mother could carry her baby in her arms. However, she also had to *want* to carry the baby, sometimes for long periods and under conditions that tried her strength and endurance.

David A. Hamburg, in his article on "Emotions in the Perspective of Human Evolution," said:

> The mother must find pleasure in holding the baby. She must experience some unpleasant feeling if she is deprived of the opportunity. This in fact turns out to be not so simple. It is a remarkable evolutionary achievement.
>
> There are several mother-infant transitions which probably served to strengthen the motivational-emotional bond — close bodily contact, nursing, smiling, patting and stroking, and rhythmic movement. The likelihood is that some or all of these situations strengthen the mother's motivation to care for her infant. Indeed it is reasonable to surmise that selection has favored infants whose behavior most effectively elicited caretaking emotional patterns in the mother.[5]

As infants were born more immature, the period of growing up had to lengthen. The approximately four years that it took a monkey to reach maturity became eight years in the chimpanzee and sixteen years in man. The time for growing up about doubled in each group.

Jane van Lawick-Goodall saw the strange effect

of differing maturity as she watched an unusual friendship develop between Gilka, a young chimp, and Goblina, a young baboon. When the two troops came fairly close together, the two young females would detach themselves and play together. After a few days of separation Gilka and Goblina would embrace and press their faces close together. The unusual friendship lasted for several months, but eventually their differential development put an end to it. At four years, Gilka was much larger than Goblina and too rough in her play for the little baboon. Another problem was that Gilka still was an exuberant adolescent, while Goblina at the same age was nearly an adult.

The biological cost of this prolongation of infancy in the ape and apeman was high. The mother had to carry or care for the infant for three or four years. During the long infancy the baby often was injured or killed.

Selection could only favor slow maturation if the advantages of prolongation (of the protected learning period) were great. But they were. The added years supplied the time to learn the skills required by the new way of life, the hunting, and the wider territory.

Youth became a protected period for learning, and what was learned — mostly through play — was exactly what was important in adult life. The young apes chasing one another, romping and charging, were practicing the behavior they would use as adults. When it came time to fight they would know every move. Flint, too, for example, watched every move as his mother Flo and his sister Fifi busily termited. His head was beside his sister's as she leaned over close to the termite mound to explore an opening she had made by scratching away the soil that sealed the burrows. Flint tried to make a tool of his own, but got it too short.

Play involves an incredible amount of repetition, and this repetition is necessary for the development of the nervous system. No one would think that a person could be good at throwing a baseball without putting a tremendous amount of time into throwing a baseball. Social skills take the same kind of repetition over the years that sports and technical skills do.

147

The sharp canines with which the mature baboon can inflict severe wounds do not erupt until the animal is about four years old. All through his earlier years the baboon has been engaging in rough play, fighting with his contemporaries, but he does not have the weapons to make his play dangerous. When he matures sexually and the teeth are fully erupted, his muscles also are ready for the serious fighting that will determine his status in the troop. By that time he also has fully mastered the techniques of fighting. It all works out together.

The young females at first also take part in the romping. By the time, however, that the male play grows rough, the young females often show more interest in the infants of the troop — for example, Fifi's attentions to her young brother Flint. Most young females are experienced infant handlers before they have any young of their own.

Communication

During the long playful years of childhood the primates also master communication, mostly by gesture and expression, though sound plays a part too.

"The apes have a large vocabulary of calls," Jane van Lawick-Goodall reported, "each signifying an emotion such as fear, pain, or pleasure. When a group arrives at a food-laden tree and gives excited 'food barks' other chimps within earshot often call in response and hurry to the feast. If one chimp gives a low uneasy 'hoo' when he sights an alarming object, others always peer in the same direction. When a youngster screams in fright or pain, his mother invariably hurries to him."

The nonverbal communication the young chimps learned was almost comically like that employed by humans. When David and his friend Goliath met one morning they embraced each other and each pressed his mouth against the other's neck. They swung up into a tree for a long period of grooming, of parting the hair and picking off bits of dried skin, or an adhering seed, or an occasional

Figure 5.6. *A charging display can help a male's rise to dominance.*

tick. They were not searching for fleas, for the wild chimpanzee does not have them.

A mature male often would pat a youngster romping near him. A touch also offered reassurance to an animal of lower rank. Flint's mother and sister would spend many minutes tickling him, to his obvious pleasure. Anger and

149

displeasure were as unmistakable. When a large male stood upright with his hair rising and uttering his loudest cries, youngsters and females learned to get out of the way. Often the terrifying appearance proved to be a bluff, but few in the way of it dared to count on this. The chimpanzees sometimes seriously cut each other in fights.

Hugo van Lawick photographed many of these expressions of emotion. No human being could mistake the pleading and begging of Fifi's outstretched hand, or Figan's big yawn, or Mike's concentrated glare just before he began a charge, or the disapproval of Rodolf's compressed lips, or Pepe's open-mouthed, wide-eyed look of excitement.

"The similarity of many chimpanzee gestures and postures to those of man is to Hugo and me one of the most exciting aspects of our study," wrote Jane van Lawick-Goodall. "It thrills us quite as much as the discovery that wild apes make and use crude tools. For either the gestures used by both man and ape have evolved along closely parallel lines or they have a common origin in some remote ancestor of both man and ape."

Again, in their long childhood the young chimps learn both what is required of them and how to get along with their elders, their contemporaries, and those younger. They become ready for social life. Without the long period for learning, the requirements of social life would have to be simpler.

Through evolution each species is so constituted that it easily learns the necessary adaptive behavior. There is then a fundamental relationship between our biology and what is a reasonable way of life. The behaviors are pleasurable to members of the species and they are practiced in play.

The young male chimpanzees are ready for adult life by the age of twelve, but they do not at once find their place in the troop of apes. They are out on the edges, though they are not denied access to sexually attractive females or to food. A young male has to establish his own place, his status, in the group. If there is an excess of males, one can migrate to another troop.

In the new australopithecine-hunter society this pattern had to be altered. As estrus and multiple-mating yielded to male-female pairs, an excess of either males or females presented problems. The extras would have been without mates, and such imbalances would have occurred with some frequency.

The hunting bands were small. In a group of forty there might be nine couples. About three infants a year would be produced, and possibly one of the three would survive to maturity. The chance was about one in eight that in a three-year period young adults might all be male or all female. Certainly departures from an equal sex ratio in such a small group would be common, and if continued the existence of the group would be threatened.

It was calculated that to maintain the 50/50 ratio needed for a smooth social life at least 100 pairs would be necessary, which would require a population of at least 500. The australopithecine bands on the savannah were quite unlikely to reach such a size. To correct the inevitable imbalance, mates would have to be found in neighboring groups. In a hunting society, the hunters would encounter them. Though the disturbance of game cannot be tolerated, many hunting societies live peaceably side by side. After some intermingling, it would be easy for a mother to suggest to her son that he might find a mate in the group from which she herself had come. Ties of custom and kinship would spring up.

The finding of mates and the production of babies under the particular conditions of human hunting and gathering favor exogamy and also the incest taboo (to prevent the birth of infants before there is a male economically able to support them).

The assumptions behind this argument are that social customs are adaptive and that nothing is more crucial for evolutionary success than the orderly production of the number of infants that can be supported. This argument also presumes that at least under extreme conditions these necessities and reasons are obvious to the people involved, as infanticide attests.

A new way of life was slowly taking shape. Place

had changed, diet had changed, and the whole social organization of the group had changed. Though the roots were present in the ancestors, these were nearly impossible changes. No other animal made them. The apemen were moving farther along the untrod way to humanity. The pace was slow, and it would depend in the end on one more major change. The outcome still was not inevitable.

6

The Thinker

For many years the theory seemed unassailable. Scientist and layman alike assumed that the enlargement of the brain first separated man from his simian ancestors. The growth of the brain, all reasoned, had to precede man's development. Was the brain of man not larger than the brain of the ape? Did the brain not constitute the critical difference between the two?

Even a forger was taken in by the theory. In the early years of this century an ambitious seeker for scientific acclaim surreptitiously buried a number of bones that he had carefully prepared to represent one of man's earliest ancestors. With considerable fanfare, he later — in 1908 — "discovered" them.

For the jaw of his "early man," the Piltdown forger — the bones were buried on the Piltdown Common in England — had chosen the jaw of a chimpanzee, although he filed down some teeth to more humanlike conformation. For the head, he obtained and meticulously aged pieces of a modern human skull.

The forger was a layman, though an informed one, who "knew" that the brain had led the way in evolution. He therefore carefully gave his early man a high-domed skull. When scientists attempted a Humpty-Dumpty restoration from the pieces, they found that the presumptive ancestor had a brain as large as that of modern man — about 1,500 cubic centimeters. This, it was generally agreed, was as it should be, and of course the apelike body that the jaw implied was also to be expected.

Some years before, in 1890, the Dutch physician Eugène Dubois had unearthed a very different kind of early creature from a riverbank in Java. A jaw fragment and a molar tooth had looked near human. But the thick, chocolate-brown cranium was low and flat — not at all as high as in a human.

The suggestion that an ancestor of·man could have had so low a skull and so receding a forehead outraged the lay and scientific worlds. Such a crude, half-ape, half-human ancestor was unthinkable. The uproar of dissent was so great that Dubois withdrew his Java finds from scientific exhibition and locked them away in a museum strong box for nearly thirty years.

Under the circumstances the Java finds did not generally upset the theory of how man evolved. The Piltdown forger did not redesign the forerunner he was creating. He still gave man the kind of ancestor man expected and felt that he deserved. Although a few scientists worried about an apelike jaw with so high a head, it was difficult to quarrel with what appeared to be the actual record from the English ground.[1]

Even in 1925 when Dart announced the discovery of the Taung baby, the old theory still prevailed. Part of the refusal to accept the six-year-old australopithecine stemmed from the continuing belief that this could not be the way it had happened. A human brain might go with a sub-human body, but surely not the other way around. The first verdict was that the South African creature was an ape.

Only as the discoveries began to come in from Sterkfontein and Kromdraai and reports belatedly issued from the laboratories, did fact overcome belief. Then the unwelcome truth emerged — man had started the long upward climb with a brain no larger than the brain of the ape. Later studies showed that long after the human line separated from the apes, the human brain remained apelike in size.

Le Gros Clark, who made the first full studies of the australopithecines, readily conceded: "the small brain-case combined with massive and projecting jaws gave a superficial resemblance to the skull of anthropoid apes."[2]

With the benefit of hindsight, the English scientist wondered a little that such apishness should have been so hard for many to accept. By the time Clark did his first work in 1947, Dubois had reopened his Java finds. Other early skulls that had come from Java and China had low skulls. All indicated essentially human bodies. Clark commented:

> It was to be expected that in still earlier and more primitive representatives of the hominid line of evolution the brain would be even smaller, perhaps hardly exceeding simian dimensions, and that the jaws would similarly be more massive and projecting in a simian fashion.
>
> In retrospect it may seem surprising that students of fossil man were not ready to accept the obvious inference that the earlier prepithecanthropine stage of hominid evolution must have been characterized by small brain-cases and massive jaws, for it was generally held that hominids and pongids were derived from a common ancestral stock and such characters of common inheritance would certainly be shown in the initial stages of hominid evolution and perhaps persisted for some time.[3]

Exacting measurements were made of the australo-pithecine skulls. Their cranial capacity ranged from 450 cc to over 550 cc, as compared to the 1,250 to 1,550 cc of modern man. Some, it is true, were broken and distorted from their long burial, but others were in a virtually perfect state of preservation, and their archaeologically impressive numbers — skulls or skull fragments from more than a hundred individuals — left no doubt that these early inhabitants of the savannah had very small brains indeed.

Were they actually in the brain size range of the great apes, as they appeared to be? The question had to be answered conclusively before any final comparison could be made. Some figures on ape brain size were of doubtful scientific validity, and there was little certainty that they were representative of the species. To provide a firm base of comparison, and not to be misled by individual variations in size, Le Gros Clark made full measurements of 100 ape skulls. His study showed the range for the gorilla, the largest brained of the anthropomorphous apes, at 340 to 683 cc. One outsize specimen was reported with a brain of 752 cc.

The first observations were confirmed. The australopithecines had not advanced in brain size beyond their ape ancestors, and the human start had been made with a small brain.

The Skulls

But brain size alone is not everything. The whole skull had to be studied, point for point. To determine where the apemen stood in evolution, Clark had to compare the skulls of apes and men. The main differences are obvious. Even the novice can immediately separate the skull of an ape from the skull of a man. In man the braincase is rounded up high and smooth, like a dome. The ape lacks both the dome and the nearly vertical forehead of man.

From the back the two are also distinctive. Man's skull reaches its maximum diameter toward the top; the ape's much farther down. And man has no sagittal crest or

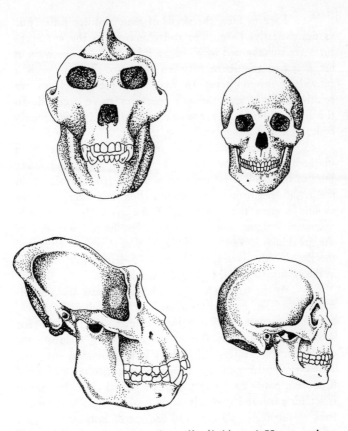

Figure 6.1. *A comparison of gorilla* (*left*) *and* Homo sapiens *skulls from the front and the side.*

protruding topknot like that of the male gorilla and orangutan and some chimpanzees. The low ape braincase does
not provide enough space for the attachment of the powerful jaw muscles, and as a result these muscles grow to the
midline of the cranium until they meet in the imposing
crest on the top. The muscles that work man's much smaller
jaw stretch only partially up the skull. Only one human
skull is known — an Eskimo with unusually large jaws —
in which the muscles grew almost to the top of the head.

Face to face, the skulls of man and ape differ just as dramatically. In gorillas and chimpanzees the eye apertures are surmounted by a craggy ridge that extends without break across the space between the eyes. The ridge is a formidable promontory. In man the eyebrow ridges are relatively slight and the eye apertures more recessed. In the cheek region, the zygomatic arch of the apes is strongly built; in man it is slender.

Nowhere though do man and ape differ more markedly than in the jaws. The massive upper and lower jaws of the ape project forward in a powerful muzzle. Even the nasal apertures nearly disappear in this long outthrust snout. In man the retraction of the jaws clearly exposes the nasal skeleton and nasal spine. The huge lower jaw of the great apes lacks the protuberant human type of chin, and the slope of the jaw varies from a 77-degree inward angle in the chimpanzee to 112 degrees in man.

At the base of the skull the differences also are unmistakable. The back of the *Homo sapiens* skull curls in long and low, something like a long helmet, whereas the ape skull is much shorter. But to the comparing scientist, one of the most revealing differences is the foramen magnum (the large opening in the occipital bone), through which the brainstem passes to connect with the spinal cord. In man it is set forward and is nearly horizontal. In apes it is farther back and deflected upward and backward. Both positions are related to posture and to the poise of the head on the top of the vertebral column. The first position reflects the upright stance of man; the latter the stooped, knuckle-walking gait of the apes.

Clark cited many other differences in the skulls of apes and men. One was particularly interesting. In apes the sutures in the skull, or the interlocking joints between the cranial bones, begin to close quite early or about when the second molar teeth erupt. In men the two halves do not finally close until about the thirtieth year and then the closing proceeds slowly.

Clark's scale had the beginnings and the *Homo*

sapiens end well marked out on it. From this base, he could appraise the australopithecine skull to judge how it was ape-like and how it was human, i.e., whether australopithecines were apes or in the human line, or more technically whether they were pongids or hominids.

As Clark studied the almost perfectly preserved skull nicknamed Mrs. Ples and other australopithecine skulls, some from young individuals and some from old, the inescapable feature was the combination of low skull and heavy jaws. This gave the australopithecines the ostensible appearance of apes. The general proportions of the skull were undeniably simian, though Clark cautioned that they were simian in approximating the level of development of the modern anthropoid apes.

But when the details of the skull were examined, the scientist met surprise after surprise. The braincase was not quite as flat as that of the apes. It was slightly rounded, though it was far from the high dome of modern man, and the highest point of the crown was elevated above the upper margin of the opening for the eye socket, almost as in modern man.

The occipital protuberances — the little bumps at the base of the skull — were low and the back neck muscles would have attached much as in man.

Most strikingly, the face lay more below the skull than in front of it. Clark was saying that, even with the low head and massive jaws, the australopithecines face to face might have looked somewhat human to a human. Artists who have attempted reconstructions using the bone measurements have invariably given them a slightly human guise.

All these features of the skull were correlated with a change in the axis formed by the column of bones at the base of the skull. Clark made the most careful studies of this section of the skull, for the bend of what he called the "basicranial axis" brought the facial skeleton to its human-like position beneath the skull and tended to diminish the massive outthrust of the jaws. It also changed the whole position of the head. This, said Clark, "allows the skull as a whole to become more perfectly balanced on top of a vertical spinal column in association with an upright posture."

A clue to the future lay in the words "in association with an upright posture." When Clark made his study, no leg or feet bones had been found. He had to base his judgment on the skull and related features. When the bones were discovered, they completely confirmed that the australopithecines had walked upright on two legs, and had departed critically from the knuckle-walking of their jungle ancestors. They were on the way to man.

Clark also pointed out that when the australopithecine skulls were examined longitudinally they contrasted with the skulls of apes. The depression for the pituitary gland was deep, as in *Homo*. The tilt of the head was less acute than in modern man, but Clark concluded that "the degree of angulation, accompanied as it is by highly significant changes in cranial proportions and relationships, is a hominid character and contrasts strongly with the Pongidae."

The apemen displayed other features that from man's vantage point could be identified as hominid. The openings for the eyes were typically human. The australopithecines looked out on the world much as men do. The palate was much closer to the human U-shape than to the ape's straight-sided alignment. The boney auditory canal was shorter than the more elongated structure in the ape skull.

As all observers had recognized, both the jaw and the grinding teeth were massive. And there was no human type of chin. Here the apemen stood with the apes.

"On the other hand," said Clark, "there is no simian shelf, and the mental foramen is displaced upward instead of near the lower margin of the jaw as it is in the Pongidae. The tooth-bearing part of the jaw is more rounded and more abbreviated than in the larger modern apes."

The skulls also revealed that the australopithecine cranial sutures were late in closing. In one skull Dart found at Makapansgat the zigzag joints were still unclosed, even though the third molar teeth had fully erupted and showed

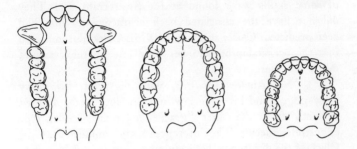

Figure 6.2. *The upper dentition of male gorilla,* Australopithecus, *and* Homo sapiens (*from left to right*).

some wear. Here the australopithecines were on the human side.

Then at Swartkrans the South African investigators discovered the different, more massive type of australopithecine they named *Australopithecus robustus.* At the top of one skull was a decided protuberance.

At first it looked very like the sagittal crest or top-knot-like protuberance of the gorilla. Some early students of the skull argued that the crest meant that these heavily built apemen would also have the neck muscles of the ape. The argument in the end proved misleading. Before the crest conclusion could be published additional sections

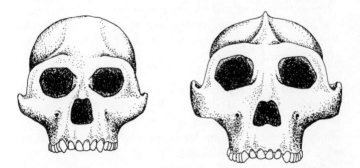

Figure 6.3. *The skulls of* Australopithecus africanus (*left*) *and* A. robustus.

163

of some skulls were found at the Swartkrans site. They did not have the associated neck characteristics that had been predicted. Closer study by Le Gros Clark also indicated that the occipital protuberances were low on the cranium, much as in man.

Nevertheless *robustus,* with his crest, his heavy brow ridges, and his huge jaw and grinding teeth, differed distinctly from the other "gracile" or more slender type of australopithecine. The differences again reminded Le Gros Clark of the differences between modern man and Neanderthal.

The evidence had piled up impressively. Clark's close study of *Australopithecus* and his meticulous comparison of him with the great apes and *Homo*, convinced him that the apemen essentially were hominids, or in the family of man, rather than pongids, and in the family of the apes.

> The essentially hominid nature of the Australopithecine skull does not depend on any single character considered as an isolated abstraction, but on the whole pattern of characters considered in combination with each other. . . .
>
> The apparently simian characters of the Australopithecine skull, such as the small braincase and the massive projecting jaw, are characters of common inheritance from a hominoid ancestry that also gave rise by divergent evolution to the modern anthropoid apes and thus do not indicate a close taxonomic relationship with the latter.[4]

Le Gros Clark was by no means denying the simian characteristics of the australopithecine skull. But the small braincase and projecting jaws, he pointed out, were simply inheritances from forebears who were apes. They were a legacy. Clark continued:

> On the other hand, the hominid characters are characters of independent acquisition, clearly demonstrating

that the australopithecines were representatives of the hominid [and not the pongid] line of evolution. In other words on the evidence of the skull alone they are to be grouped within the evolving trend of the Hominidae and taxonomically therefore are to be included in the family.[5]

On the evidence of the skull, Le Gros Clark therefore put the australopithecines in the human race, and in effect named them as our immediate forebears, perhaps founders. However low of brow and small of brain, they had left their simian ancestors behind. They were in effect new creatures moving toward an unforeseeable future, and leaving a lower animal past. A gap never before crossed had been bridged.

The Brain

What specifically enabled the small-brained australopithecines to live as no others had before them? They were the first to chip a fist-sized piece of stone and make it into a useful weapon, and to carry a piece of stone from one place to another where it could be used more conveniently.

Animals as accomplished as the apes might have been expected to discover the use of stone tools. It would have seemed only one more step. And yet the failure of all except the australopithecines to take that step indicated that it was not a small additional skill, but a matter of another magnitude, and probably impossible without special intelligence.

In the jungle the chimpanzee's use of a twig for terminting — even the selection of the twig — does not determine survival. An ape can live very well without the termite tidbits, and the most skilled termiters are not necessarily the parents of the next generation. Chimpanzees do not live by termiting alone. Thus no selective pressure favors those making the best use of tools. The part of the chimpanzee brain governing hand movements grew no larger. In fact it continued to be no larger than the foot area.

Out on the arid savannah and away from the lush food of the jungle different pressures prevailed. The creature best able to chip a stone and use it to kill food had a vital advantage. A kill might make the difference between life and starvation. The toolmaker was more likely to live long enough to produce offspring, and the slightly better brain that enabled him to make the tools was perhaps passed on to the next generation.

The pressure, though, or the advantage of toolmaking in that world of long ago, may have been slight, for the development of the brain and toolmaking beyond that australopithecine start was inordinately slow. For most of the 3 million or more years that the australopithecines are now known to have lived, they made only the same simple pebble tools. Whether they lived in South Africa, or in the Olduvai Gorge, or in what is now Ethiopia, the three areas where their remains have so far been found, their tools were essentially the same. Their brains grew little larger. Their way of life was stable; perhaps the most stable of them all.

Enlargement of the Brain

When enlargement of the brain began, possibly in the era of 1,000,000 to 500,000 years ago, much of the growth was in the thick whitish carpet of nerve cells that covers the cerebral hemispheres. The dome of the skull grew high, but the space for the growing cortex still was strictly limited. Like any carpet crowded into too small a space the cortex continued to crinkle and crumble into furrows or fissures. In the modern brain only about 35 per cent of the cells are estimated to lie on the brain surface. The others are infolded, forming the banks of the fissures.

But this growth that ultimately would triple the size of the australopithecine brain was not simply a generalized enlargement of the old brain. Some areas grew much more than others, crowding the old sensory and motor areas ever deeper into the fissures. The new areas were essentially the outgrowth of certain areas of gray matter in the older brainstem, the early small brain.

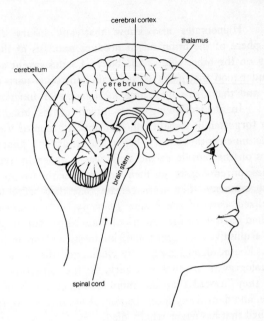

Figure 6.4. *The human brain with the parts referred to in the text labelled.*

For many centuries the development of the brain was unknown, as was the role of the brain itself. The Sumerians and Babylonians believed that the liver was the seat of the intellect. Others placed the mind in the heart, and we still talk of "taking life's lessons to heart." Hippocrates, in the fifth century B.C., undertook to challenge the deeply rooted conviction about the heart.

"Some people say," wrote Hippocrates, "that the heart is the organ with which we think and that it feels pain and anxiety. But it is not so. . . . Men ought to know that it is from the brain and the brain alone that arise our pleasures, joys, laughter and jests, as well as our sorrows, pains, griefs, and tears. Through it in particular, we think, see, hear, and distinguish the ugly from the beautiful, the pleasant from the unpleasant."

167

Hippocrates also knew that any injury to one hemisphere of the brain might produce paralysis of the arm or leg on the other side of the body. To this extent at least he understood that parts of the brain controlled parts of the body and that there was some localization of function.

In the following years much of his insight was either forgotten or disbelieved. Not until a group of Viennese in the nineteenth century began to study the knobs and bumps on the outside of the skull was it generally recalled. As these phrenologists ran their fingers over the irregularities of the braincase they were certain that they were feeling specialized areas of the brain. They not only claimed that they had discovered the centers of knowledge, but of mother love, acquisitiveness, aggression, kindness, and other human traits. The academicians quickly challenged the work of the phrenologists as so much quackery. At the same time, however, they insisted that the mind dwelt in the brain as a whole, and denied any specialization. A brain controversy was launched that has never wholly died.

In the 1860's a patient who had lost his power of speech came to the French surgeon Paul Broca. Otherwise he seemed to be unaffected. After his death Broca performed an autopsy and found a lesion in the left hemisphere of the brain. Damage at one specific point apparently had destroyed the man's ability to speak. It looked as though Broca had located the center of speech. In 1861 he reported that the point was situated in the general region of the third frontal convolution. This became known as "Broca's area," and science was off on a new trail. Two persons involved in brain research, Miller Penfield and Lamar Roberts, wrote:

> It is almost a century since Broca showed that speech had some degree of neuronal localization in the brain. He demonstrated that what he called aphemia and what we now call aphasia was produced by a relatively small destruction of a certain area of the cortex in the dominant hemisphere of a man. This meant, of course, not that speech was located there in the sense of a phrenologist's localization, but that the area in question

was used as an essential part of a functional mechanism employed while the individual spoke. It showed further that a man could still think and carry out other forms of voluntary activity while the speech mechanism was paralyzed. The clock still ran, although the chimes had been silenced.[6]

Another nineteenth-century experiment further opened the way into the study of the brain as it is and as it has evolved. In 1870, G. Fritsch and E. Hitzig applied an electric current to the lightly anaesthetized brain of a dog. As they touched one side of the cerebral cortex with an electrode an opposite leg moved. By studying the brain itself and by using electric current, the strange but all-controlling brain could be explored.

Penfield and Roberts went far in mapping the brain in a series of operations in the 1950's. Whether they were operating to repair an injury or to remove a tumor or to excise an area producing epileptic seizures, they needed to know as exactly as possible what the effects would be. Would the operation interfere with such essentials as speech, and movement?

Only a local anaesthetic was used in their operations, for there is no sensation of pain in the brain. As the surgeons exploratively touched an area of the brain with their electrodes the fully conscious patient could report what he saw and felt.

A thirty-seven-year-old man after receiving a blow on the right side of the skull suffered severe epileptic seizures during the next six years. An operation was recommended. After the skull was opened, the surgeon touched a point in a central area. The patient felt a tingling in his right hand. The doctor then placed a tiny square of paper labeled with a clearly readable "1" at the point on the patient's brain where the response had been produced. At another point the man said, "I had a feeling in my throat which stopped my speech." Another number was placed. At another point of stimulation the patient hesitated and then said, "butterfly." Another tiny square of paper went down. At the next point the patient called out, "Oh, I know what that is. That is what you put in your shoe." After the electrode was withdrawn he said, "foot."

Thirty little numbered slips of paper went down on the cortex of the living brain something like a meandering row of square, numbered buttons. The doctor had his map of what areas could be interfered with and what he had to avoid. Such operations repeated many times marked out the major areas of the brain and its areas of specialization.

The doctors delineated the motor area, the primary receiving and transmitting center for all the motions of the body. In this crucial section the doctors discovered an amazing and explicit sequence. At one end lay an area controlling the toes. It was followed in order by areas for the ankle, knee, hip, trunk, and shoulder. Of all these centers, that for the ankle was by far the largest; ankle and toe areas together were larger than those for the hip, knee, and trunk combined.

Next in the motor sequence came the elbow and wrist area, and then the very large hand section, which outstripped all the other arm areas.

Sections followed in order, controlling the little finger, the ring, middle, and index fingers, and the thumb. Their separateness made it easy for humans, unlike some other primates, to move each finger separately. Some apes must move all the fingers or none. Only man thus has the ability to play the piano or operate a typewriter. Moving fingers independently is one of the special gifts. The brain areas controlling the hand and fingers together were much larger than the areas for the body and legs.

Next came the extensive areas relating to the mouth. The area for the lips was as large as that for the hand, with additional sections for the jaw, tongue, and swallowing. The physicians tested these areas repeatedly. Whenever they touched one with an electrode, invariably the muscle it controlled moved or responded — whether the lips, or little finger, or toes. "The sequence of responses to electrical stimulation on the cortex, along the motor strip

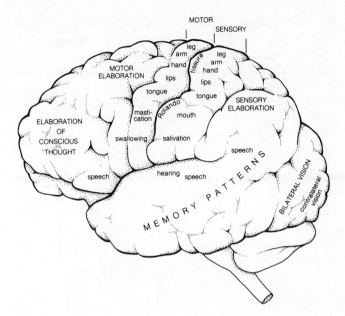

Figure 6.5. *A summary of the functions of the cortex. Note how much is concerned with hand skills and speech. The brain also controls the emotions, making orderly social life possible.*

from toes through arm and face to swallowing is unvaried from one individual to the next," said Penfield and Roberts. It was universal, the heredity of all.

Just across from the motor area, on the opposite side of the fissure, lay the somatic, or feeling, or sensation strip. Sensations fed into the area were transmitted out of it through the deeper areas of the brain, but the sequence occurred again on the cortex — toes, foot, leg, hip, trunk, neck, head, shoulder, arm, elbow, forearm, wrist, hand, little finger, ring, middle and index fingers, thumb, eyes, nose, face, upper lip, lower lip, teeth, gums and jaw, tongue, inside of mouth, and intraabdominal muscles. A touch on this cortex in one area produced an immediate sensation in the corresponding part of the body and a sense of the position of that part of the body.

171

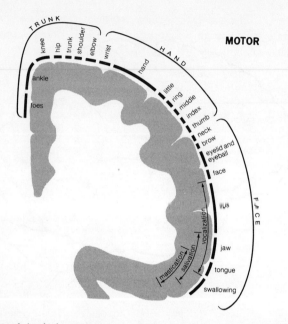

Figure 6.6. *A functional map of the motor cortex; the human brain is shown in a cross section. The brackets show the large areas involved with hand and facial motor responses. Localization is not a set of fixed points, but emphasis; the area for the thumb, for example, is where stimulation is most likely to cause the thumb to move, but other responses may come from the area, too.*

In a human figure proportioned to the size of the brain's motor areas, the imaginary body would look all hand and mouth. All other parts shrink into relative insignificance. This motor profile of a human reveals what was important in the evolution of man.

A similar homunculus (or human representation) of the sensory areas makes the imaginary figure one of lips and hands (including fingers). Even the eye is tiny in comparison to the fulsome, exaggerated lips. The hand and tongue too are far out of normal proportion. In sensation and in the brain areas controlling the sense, the lips and hands are dominant. In taste and feeling modern man is largely lips, tongue, and hands.

The ape did not share these enlargements or exaggerations of certain old areas of the cortex. They were the added emoluments; the constructions of evolution. They also were exactly the developments that set man apart from the ape, for they were the basis of the uniquely skilled hands and the speech that are man's alone. They were the last added, the newest, but they made the difference.

Other Brain Evidence

The new studies of the brain, added to the old ones, had clearly marked the areas added after the appearance of the australopithecines. They demonstrated what brain developments had made a one-time ape into a human.

There is no direct way to study the brain areas or the brain specializations of the australopithecines. Time left only the fossilized bone of the skull. Nevertheless, one clue is direct. The cerebellum, literally the little or diminutive brain lying back of and below the cerebrum, is associated partly with learned hand movements. In man it is three times larger than in the apes, and the part of it that is enlarged is the part dealing specifically with the hand movements.

The size of the cerebellum can be estimated from the size and form of a skull, and sufficient australopithecine material is available to make such estimates. The skulls of the apemen show clearly that the australopithecines did not have the space in their low-domed skulls either for a large cerebellum or for a large area of motor cortex.

The size of the brain, however, is not the sole test of mental ability. One of the whales has a brain of more than 10,000 cc. For all its great bulk, it constitutes only one gram of brain substance for each 8,500 grams of body, while modern man has one gram of brain for each 44 grams of body weight. But neither is the latter measurement an absolute. The capuchin monkey has one gram of brain for each 17.5 grams of body. The noted anthropologist Franz Weidenreich maintained with little contradiction that a brain may be judged only by the use made of it and that cultural objects are the only reliable evidence of such use. The australopithecines' cultural objects are principally their chipped stone tools.

Nevertheless the low dome and the small cerebellum area suggest strongly that making tools was far more difficult for the apemen than for their larger-brained descendants. That the australopithecines made little change in their chipped pebbles for 3 million years or more underwrote the physical evidence of a small, apelike brain.

How did the enlarged brain areas come to be? Why did only man develop them? Why did other apes not follow a similar course? The answer is that the success of a new way of life created new selection pressures which ultimately caused the evolution of new neural structures.

In the case of tool-using the success of this class of behavior in the early human lineage led to selection for ease of learning (including interest in objects and exploration), skillful use, practice through play, and more complex communication.

The Motor Way

Evolution was affected not so much by learning to put a sharp edge on a piece of stone as by the whole way of life the use of the tool brought with it. Motor skill was part of a behavioral complex.

To throw a rock — a motor skill — requires practice, and this has to be rewarding and pleasurable. Jane van Lawick-Goodall once watched Mr. Worzle, a chimpanzee, throw three times in succession with what she described as "a beautiful overarm throw." He twice hit a big male baboon about three feet away. But his weapons were a handful of leaves, a banana skin, and a small pebble. He scarcely inflicted enough damage to induce him to try it again.

Although few female chimps threw objects, Fifi in her sixth year became quite a flinger of missiles. She would gather up a handful of pebbles and charge toward an animal that had annoyed her. Her aim, however, was decidedly poor, and the stones fell on her own head about as often as on her intended victim.

Again there was little reward in throwing and little incentive to practice it. In a cage where the situation is unchanging and offers few diversions a chimpanzee, as previously noted, may develop a fair degree of accuracy in hitting some unwary human with anything at hand for throwing. But the young human does not have to be caged to find throwing to his liking. He probably wins praise for doing it well and will throw the ball at some target over and over.

The scientists conclude that the greatest encouragement in learning any skill is the appreciation of others. Approval is so basic and necessary to developing any skill that many overlook the fact that only man cheers on his youngsters and contemporaries. No other primate stands by and applauds success. The baby chimp observed by Jane van Lawick-Goodall watched every move made by his sister as she fished for termites. He tried himself, although at first he did not get the twigs the right length. At no point did his sister help him or urge him on. He had to learn without her assistance and entirely by copying her actions.

Conscious social encouragement and facilitation of learning is unique to man. Both are essential for learning skills which require long practice. For example the infant human learns in games, and success is applauded and socially rewarded. If a young chimpanzee throws, it is an isolated event with no immediate social reward to repeat or to practice. The brain makes possible the social situation and communication which lead to full development of the motor skills.

Without reward, without encouragement, and without practice the apes living in the jungle did not develop enlarged motor areas in the brain. As all three came in with a new way of life on the savannahs, new selective pressures favored larger brains. It all went together.

175

More Complex Communication

The use of tools and the new mode of life favored the evolution of more complex communication, another specialization that made man.

It was not that the apes and other animals could not communicate quite effectively with one another. The van Lawick-Goodall chimpanzees moved fast when big J. B., their leader, uttered a scream of alarm or rage. Figan also well understood the cries of his little brother Flint when Flint's baby legs could not reach the branch below him. Flint in his turn responded to the pleased or angry grunts of his mother Flo. Apparently little brain is required for nonlinguistic communication. By sound and gesture the non-human primates convey a wide range of information and feeling. But such sounds and gestures are not language. They are not explicit references to the environment.

Scientists who have observed the apes in the wild frequently have seen the leader of a troop warn others that a predator is near. But the ape has no cry to say "lion." At the most he can tell the troop either that a terrestrial or an arboreal enemy is approaching. He has one distinctive sound for danger from above and another for danger from below, and the understanding troop will drop to the ground to play dead or rapidly climb into the trees. Beyond this point the ape's communication does not and cannot go. Only man can call out "lion" and name the danger.

Nothing in the structure of the ape's mouth or larynx prevents speech. Scientists, well aware of these structural possibilities, have spent many years trying to teach chimpanzees to talk. They have raised them along with a child, giving both the same training in speech. The child learned readily and was soon full of words that brought him what he wanted, from a trip outdoors, to the petting of a friendly dog, to food, and ultimately full-scale communication with others. The ape did not. And this is true of all human children, living in all parts of the world from the most remote and wild to the most urbanized. All can learn a language or several languages. The answer, as it finally was learned, is that the child has the brain areas that make speech possible. The apes lack these elaborated areas.[7]

Also, the articulatory apparatus in man and in ape does differ; probably the brain is much more important. The brain controls meaning and the sound code, but the precise sounds are produced by the pharynx and its associated structures.

Then how did the ape's effective but nonlinguistic communication develop into the human's speech? And why did speech develop only once in a world where many had voices and all the vocal equipment for language? Did the australopithecines have speech?

So far no evidence has been found that the australopithecine brain had the structures for speech. Perhaps the apemen hunting on the savannah and dragging their kill back to camp communicated mostly by gestures and postures supplemented by sounds rather than words.

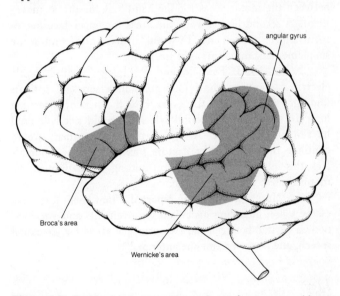

Figure 6.7. *Brain speech areas are on the surface on one side; a subsurface bundle of nerve fibers apparently transmits auditory patterns from Wernicke's area to Broca's.*

Probably language came as slowly as improved tool use. Millions of years may have passed between the first use of verbal symbols and the evolution of languages of the complexity of those in use today. Scholars, in fact, have estimated that most languages of today made their appearance only about 40,000 years ago, or that they emerged at about the same time as *Homo sapiens* himself.

Certainly the first apemen to use sounds to convey a specific meaning would have had an advantage. The first crude calls that could convey the idea "lion" instead of simply "danger" may have saved lives and changed the selective pressures on the nervous system, muscles, and brain. Those able to make such use of the voice might well have been the survivors.

Slowly, over countless generations, whole specialized speech areas developed in the australopithecine descendants, and in no other animal. Only man has the four brain areas that produce vocalization as speech. One area is located between the motor areas for the hand and for throat movement. A second lies between the areas for upper face movement and lip movement. Two similar areas are found in the supplementary motor areas of the brain.

In 1950, Penfield and Rasmussen applied gentle electric currents to these four areas in a series of patients undergoing operations. In every case the patient uttered a long drawn-out vowel sound which he could not halt until he ran out of breath. After breathing, the patient would continue the sound. The doctors found that other animals lack this inborn vocalization transmitting mechanism in the motor cortex. It is man's alone.

"It is evident," they reported, "that cortical control of the voice, including articulatory movements and vocalization, is located between the two principal areas for ideational speech, one posterior and one anterior."[8]

Ideas

As their findings indicated, another area in which the ideas expressed in speech are organized was part of the development of speech. They also were able to map these areas and learned that if the ideational areas are lost, speech is gone.

All the areas of the brain involving speech and related functions proved to be elaborations of the "older brain," the gray matter in the brainstem and thalamus. Much of the coordination and integration of speech with the general functioning of the brain apparently still takes place in the older, deeper sections.

"It is proposed as a speech hypothesis that the functions of all three cortical areas in man are coordinated by projections of each to parts of the thalamus and by means of these circuits the elaboration of speech is somehow carried out," Penfield and Roberts wrote.[9]

They arrived at their conclusions by evidence developed in the operations. If they removed brain matter just beyond the boundaries of the speech areas there was no more than a transient post-operative interference with speech. The connections with the rest of the brain apparently were not made through the bordering areas, but through the underlying, deeper, older areas of the brain. Additional proof was supplied that the speech areas were additional, and outgrowths of the older brain.

Memory

Along with the growth of the speech areas the areas dealing with memory increased. The memory areas still have not been as closely mapped as the other new areas, but the surgeons found that when a wide, general area was stimulated memories were stirred.

As the surgeons touched the memory area of one patient, he exclaimed: "Yes, Doctor, now I hear people laughing — my friends in South Africa." He felt that he was again with his friends at the party he was reexperiencing, and began to give some more details. If the stimulus had been continued, the doctors were certain that the experience would have continued to unroll, moment by moment. They compared such an unfolding of memory to running a strip of cinematographic film on which is registered everything that the individual has experienced. As on a film, there is no turning back and no crossing over to other periods. When the electrodes were withdrawn, the experience or memory stopped as suddenly as it had begun. In the memory area of the brain, it became apparent, is a neuronal record of the individual's stream of consciousness.

"On the thread of time are strung, like pearls, an unending succession of meaningful patterns that can still recall the vanished content of a former awareness," said Penfield and Roberts. "No man can voluntarily reactivate that record. . . . It is, it seems to me, in the mechanism of recall and comparison and interpretation that the interpretive cortex of the temporal lobe plays its specialized role."[10] Again, the ape brain has no similar enlarged memory areas.

Society

The evolution of motor skills, of learning, and communication was linked inseparably with the development of a more complex society. Only the transfer of information made such a society possible, and without close social ties communication could not have developed to its full extent. Again all depended upon the evolution of the brain.

The functions of the brain that are linked with society are described as the "social brain." This is the complex of parts that make human social life possible and distinguishes it from the social life of monkeys and apes.

The biological base had to be there, though the culture was learned. Control also had to go with it. When an ape becomes angry he may run down a hill tearing branches from the bushes and hurling everything that comes to his hand. In such a rage he is terrifying to man and beast. Jane van Lawick-Goodall often watched a whole troop take refuge in the trees as a big male put on one of his formidable displays of rage.

But a more complex society cannot function if its members constantly run amuck. Selection led to the survival of those with some better degree of control over rage.

Ultimately areas were added to the brain that brought the rawest and most violent emotions under a considerable degree of control. Then societies could develop.

As Charles Darwin early recognized, many of the basic emotions are the same in animals and humans. Even their expression is often the same. Terror causes men, apes, and members of the lower groups of animals to tremble. The heart palpitates and the hair stands on end. The love of a mother for her young is common to all. Jane van Lawick-Goodall repeatedly noted Flo's careful attention to her offspring, and much earlier Darwin remarked that orphan monkeys are always adopted and cared for by other members of the troop, both male and female. One baboon which Darwin observed adopted young dogs or cats whenever she had the chance. When one of her adopted kittens scratched her, she immediately examined its feet and promptly bit off its claws, but continued to give it tender loving care.

Darwin also argued that most of what he called the "higher emotions" are shared by man and the other animals. He cited a dog's jealousy if his master's attention is lavished on some other animal.

In a test of a monkey's curiosity Darwin once carried a stuffed snake into the monkey house at the Zoological Gardens. "The excitement caused was one of the most curious spectacles I ever beheld," he said. Some monkeys dashed about uttering sharp cries of alarm. Darwin then placed his stuffed snake on the ground. After a while, all the monkeys nervously gathered around it in a circle, staring intently at the puzzling and frightening thing. Darwin later tried them with a dead fish, a mouse, and a living turtle. Before long, they were handling all three.

Later he took in a small live snake in a partly open paper bag. One monkey soon edged up, took a peek, and fled. Then monkey after monkey, each with head held high and turned to one side, took a momentary look at the fearsome object in the bag.

Darwin also argued that animals have excellent memories. Darwin had owned a dog before he left on his five-year voyage around the world on the *Beagle*. Upon his return he went to the stable where the dog lived and shouted to him in his old manner. "He shewed no joy," Darwin reported, "but instantly followed me out walking and obeyed exactly as if I had parted with him only half an hour before."

Darwin also saw much evidence that animals are capable of intelligence and reason. A monkey was given lumps of sugar wrapped in paper. An experimenter concealed a wasp in one lump. As the monkey removed the wrapping in the usual way, he was stung. But this happened only once. Thereafter before opening a lump of sugar the monkey held the packet to his ear to detect any movement in it. He remembered and took a reasonable precaution.

Darwin was trying to establish that the emotions and mental abilities of man as well as his physical structure could have evolved from the lower animals. "There can be no doubt," he wrote in *The Descent of Man*, "that the difference between the mind of the lowest man and that of the highest animal is immense. . . . Nevertheless the difference . . . great as it is, certainly is one of degree and not of kind.

"We have seen that the senses and intuitions, the various emotions and faculties, such as love, memory, attention, curiosity, imitation, etc., of which man boasts, may be found in an incipient or sometimes even in a well developed condition in the lower animals."

Darwin himself did not go into a detailed study of the brain, but in later editions of the *Descent of Man* he included a note written in 1874 by his friend and defender, the eminent biologist Thomas H. Huxley.

There remains no dispute as to the resemblance in fundamental character between the ape's brain and man's, nor any as to the wonderfully close similarity between the chimpanzee, orang, and man in even the details of the arrangement of the gyri and culci of the cerebral hemispheres. Nor turning to the differences between the brains of the highest apes and that of man, is there any serious question as to the nature and extent of these differences. It is admitted that man's cerebral hemispheres are absolutely and relatively larger than those of the orangs and chimpanzees.

Huxley also reemphasized the finding with which he had startled and angered much of the world in 1863. As far as the brain's structure goes, he said, it is clear that man differs less from the chimpanzee or orangutan than either of these apes do from the monkeys. "The difference between the brain of the chimpanzee and man is almost insignificant when compared with that between the chimpanzee brain and that of a lemur," he said.

The new studies of the brain have thoroughly underwritten Huxley's and Darwin's arguments and findings. The brains of many mammals and particularly of the apes are alike in general organization; the difference lies in the development of certain areas.

Penfield and Roberts made the same point: "The brain of the dog resembles the human brain in general organization. The brain of the chimpanzee is even more like ours. All of the lobes are present. The pathways and muscular control are similar. Chimpanzee and dog have large areas of cerebral cortex like our own, used for seeing, hearing, feeling. They even have larger areas for smelling."[11]

For a while, the scientists also saw, children and chimpanzees learn in much the same way. Both learn the meaning of whatever is around them. Both also learn from experience to understand certain concepts, such as eating and going outside. Both, up to a point, understand certain other concepts expressed in words or gestures, possibly the word "no" or the nod of "yes."

All this changes when the child begins to speak. Then the chimpanzee can no longer follow. The chimp chatters or makes other noises by using neurological motor mechanisms in the "old brain." The child talks by making use of the added new speech sections of the brain.

At what time in history man learned to talk and developed the society and way of life that went with it is now unknown. Whether or not it happened in australopithecine time, now set at 4 million to 1 million years ago, no one

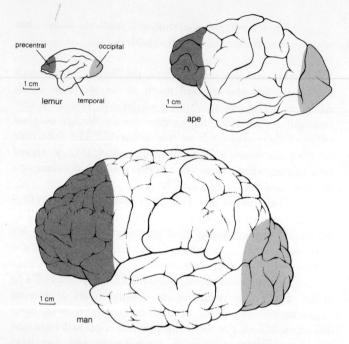

Figure 6.8. *The brains of three primates show the differences in development of certain areas. The area concerned with vision (occipital lobe) is large in them all. The motor control area (precentral cortex) is larger in ape and man. The temporal lobe is more complex and larger in the higher primates.*

can positively say. The chances are, however, that modern man would not find his australopithecine forebears very bright. In all probability their behavior also could have been understood better on the chimpanzee than on the human level. They were in short apemen, or man-apes.

Even the earliest known of the in-between creatures had nevertheless departed far from its immediate ape ancestors. The australopithecines alone crossed the divide that ultimately set man aside from his predecessors and from all the millions of other animals that live today or have lived in the past. However primitive, some characteristics that we ascribe to man have been added to the apes of the early jungle.

By 10 million to 5 million years ago when some venturesome apes moved out onto the dry plains and managed to survive in a new way of life, the brain had reached about 450 to 550 cc — the size of the ape brain then and now.

The earliest apemen so far discovered, those dated at 3 to 4 million years ago, possessed brains in this size range. It was a small brain, though still a remarkable one in comparison with any other.

No evidence of much change has been discovered thus far during the next 2.5 million years. Wherever the apemen spread they made only their simple chipped stone tools. Progress was slow. Untold generations lived much as their ancestors had, as small bands of hunters, perhaps faring so well in their limited though widening world that no change was required for survival.

Nevertheless a few must have pressed on into new lands and more rigorous climates. By 500,000 years ago men whose brains had increased to nearly 1,000 cc were living in Asia and had reached its outer extensions in Java. With their doubled brains they made more complex tools and the chipped pebbles of their ancestors were largely forgotten. They knew fire, for their hearths have been found, and they killed larger animals on their hunts.

The pace of change was beginning to step up. Only 450,000 years later — about 50,000 years ago — another kind of man had appeared in many parts of the world. His brain had reached the modern range, 1,250 to about 1,550 cc. It was triple the brain of his forerunner, the australopithecine.

After that the brain grew no larger, but the pace of change accelerated even faster, through the Bronze and Iron Ages to modern civilization with its three billions occupying all parts of the globe and crowded into great agglomerations called cities.

Impossible? Even though plentiful fossils attest to the change that occurred from ape to man, even though the evolution took some 5 million to 10 million years, is it possible to comprehend how it happened?

Only now, as the newest findings demonstrate that

the change from ape to man was not total but partial, have the realities of this evolution become explainable. Now it can be seen in summary and with growing certainty that our evolution was a mosaic.

As a few apes left the jungle, and the most bipedal and upright survived in the new terrain, their legs grew longer and the foot and pelvis changed. But at first there was little change in the low dome of the head, in the small brain, and almost no change in the trunk, in its breadth, in the shortness of the lumbar region, or in the length of arms. Most bones, joints, and muscles remained as they had been through most of the time of the apes.

Hands then began to change. Those best able to manipulate the chipped stone tools and win themselves more food had a decided advantage. The hand bones found by Leakey at Olduvai Gorge are about halfway in form between those of contemporary man and the modern apes. The thumb was growing longer and was capable of a powerful grasp.

But, as the accumulating new research dramatically demonstrates, little changed inside. The quantity of DNA did not change. The hemoglobin, that essential of life, continued exactly the same. There was little alteration in the cytochromes, the albumins, the transferrins. The apemen still were apes in their blood, their chemistry, and much of their bodies — as the survival of this blood, chemistry, and bodily form in their descendants proves.

Only the changes in the legs and feet that made it possible for the australopithecines to walk and run on two legs instead of the ancestral four, and the related changes in the hand and teeth, set them decisively apart from the apes. Nevertheless these changes made possible a new way of life and a new kind of selection.

No total reshaping or remaking was necessary then to turn ape into man. A relatively few biological changes with long and large social consequences made the transition from ape to apeman. And only a few more biological changes, most particularly the tripling in the size of the brain and its

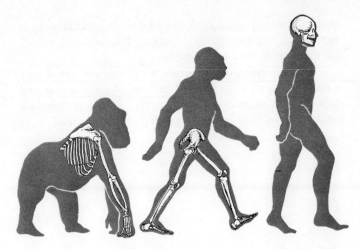

Figure 6.9. *These drawings depict the evolution of the three skeletal segments.*

development of highly specialized areas, had to follow to convert apemen into *Homo sapiens*. And even the tripling of the brain required only the enlargement of already established areas of the old brain.

It long seemed nearly incredible that man could have evolved from a knuckle-walking, ham-handed, non-speaking wild ape of the jungle. Charles Darwin proved to a shocked world that the transition had occurred and he demonstrated that the means was natural selection. This left unanswered the pressing question: how specifically, how did it happen? That question seemed forever beyond answering, for it could not be answered by the fossils or comparative studies alone.

But now biological and chemical and other studies have unexpectedly revealed for the first time how man has changed — or not changed — inwardly. Even the time of the change can be estimated.

Far less change than anticipated was required to convert ape into man, for in many aspects man remained essentially apelike. The obvious and well-known differences

187

that so positively distinguish the two — their differences in appearance — came late in evolution. The ancestral, hereditary similarities tend to be hidden.

However great or small, the changes occurred only once. Only once out of untold millions of opportunities and over millions of years did man evolve. This feat happened only once and only lately in the long expanse of time.

Notes

Chapter 1

1. Adam Sedgwick, Darwin's former professor of geology, in a letter to Darwin, in Francis Darwin, *The Life and Letters of Charles Darwin* (New York: D. Appleton & Co., 1887), p. 44.

2. A. C. Wilson and V. M. Sarich, Departments of Biochemistry and Anthropology, University of California, Berkeley, "A Molecular Time Scale for Human Evolution," 1969.

3. Morris Goodman, "Effects of Evolution on Primate Macromolecules," *Primates* 8 (1967): 1–22.

4. G. William Moore and Morris Goodman, "Phylogeny and Taxonomy of the Catarrhine Primates," in *Taxonomy and Phylogeny of Old World Primates*, B. Chiarelli, ed. (Torino: Rosenberg & Sellier, 1968), p. 123.

5. Vincent M. Sarich, "The Phylogeny of the Cercopithecoidea," 1969.

6. Moore and Goodman, "Phylogeny and Taxonomy," p. 121.

7. Wilson and Sarich, "A Molecular Time Scale for Human Evolution."

Chapter 2

1. See Jane van Lawick-Goodall, *My Friends the Wild Chimpanzees* (Washington, D.C.: The National Geographic Society, 1967), esp. chaps. 1, 2, and 5, and *In the Shadow of Man* (Boston: Houghton Mifflin, 1971), esp. chaps. 3–6. The data on the succeeding pages is drawn from the chapters cited above.

2. George B. Schaller, *The Year of the Gorilla* (Chicago: University of Chicago Press, 1964). The passages quoted in this section come from pages 201–210.

3. Phyllis C. Jay, ed., *Primates* (New York: Holt, Rinehart & Winston, 1968), p. 488.

4. Ibid., p. 499.

5. Elwyn L. Simons, *Primate Evolution* (New York: Macmillan, 1972).

Chapter 3

1. Our gratitude to Kenneth Page Oakley for the chapter title, "Tools Makyth Man," Smithsonian Report (Washington, D.C., 1958), pp. 431–445.

2. In Phyllis C. Jay, ed., *Primates* (New York: Holt, Rinehart & Winston, 1968), p. 501.

3. Jane B. Lancaster, "On the Evolution of Tool Using Behavior," *American Anthropology* 70, no. 1 (February 1968): 55–66.

4. Ibid., p. 58.

5. Elwyn L. Simons, *Primate Evolution* (New York: Macmillan, 1972).

Chapter 4

1. Dr. Raymond A. Dart, with Dennis Craig, *Adventures with the Missing Link* (New York: Harper & Brothers, 1959), pp. 35–36.

2. Ibid., pp. 49–50.

3. Ibid., p. 54.

4. Robert Broom, *Finding the Missing Link* (London: C. A. Watts & Co., 1950), p. 39.

5. Ibid., p. 55.

6. See Chapter One.

7. See Raymond A. Dart, *Adventures with the Missing Link* (New York: Harper & Brothers, 1959), p. 36.

8. The generic name *Zinjanthropus* was later abandoned and the skull renamed *Australopithecus boisei*.

9. Sir Wilfred E. Le Gros Clark, *Man-Apes or Ape-Men?* (New York: Holt, Rinehart & Winston, 1967), pp. 45–47.

10. Ibid., p. 48.

Chapter 5

1. John Napier, "The Evolution of the Hand," *Scientific American* 207, no. 6 (December 1962): 62.

2. Richard B. Lee and Irven De Vore, eds., *Man the Hunter* (Chicago: Aldine, 1968); see the article by Sherwood L. Washburn and C. S. Lancaster, pp. 293–303.

3. S. L. Washburn, Phyllis C. Jay, and Jane B. Lancaster, "Field Studies of Old World Monkeys and Apes," *Science* 150 (December 17, 1965): 1541–1547.

4. Andy P. Wilson and R. C. Boelkins, "Evidence for Seasonal Variation in Aggressive Behavior by Macaques," *Animal Behavior* 18 (1970) : 719–724.

5. In Peter H. Knapp, *Expression of the Emotions in Man* (New York: International Universities Press, 1963), chap. 16.

Chapter 6

1. Not until 1953 was the hoax definitely proved and announced.

2. Sir Wilfred E. Le Gros Clark, *Man-Apes or Ape-Men?* (New York: Holt, Rinehart & Winston, 1967), p. 65.

3. Ibid., p. 66.

4. Ibid., pp. 85–86.

5. Ibid., p. 86.

6. Wilder Penfield and Lamar Roberts, *Speech and Brain Mechanisms* (Princeton, N.J.: Princeton University Press, 1959), p. 14.

7. The chimpanzee has been taught to communicate with sign language and with colored discs. In both cases human intervention is necessary.

8. Wilder Penfield and Theodore Rasmussen, *Cerebral Cortex of Man* (New York: Macmillan, 1950).

9. Penfield and Roberts, *Speech and Brain Mechanisms*, p. 212.

10. Ibid., pp. 54–55.

11. Ibid., p. 24.

Index

193